MW00931340

Tales of the Undaunted

Tales of the Undaunted

LEGEND OF JOSH EPPS

Curtis Meeks

A NOVEL OF THE WESTERN FRONTIER

This book is a work of fiction. Characters, names, places and incidents either are products of the author's imagination or are used fictitiously. The major events, rendezvous, wagon trains, Civil War, Texas Rangers are historically accurate.

Library of Congress Number: 2004090465
ISBN: Hardcover 1-4134-4683-3
Softcover 1-4134-4682-5

This book was printed in the United States of America.

To order additional copies of this book, contact:
Xlibris Corporation
1-888-795-4274
www.Xlibris.com
Orders@Xlibris.com

21356

Contents

To my wife, Janie, who
filled my heart with love and
kindness for sixty-three years,
I dedicate this book.

Characters

JOSH EPPS

- MOUNTAIN MAN / BEAVER TRAPPER
- WAGONEER
- WAGON TRAIN GUIDE / SCOUT
- DROVER
- CATTLE BARON

WILL PURDY

- TEXAS RANGER
- INDIAN FIGHTER
- CONFEDERATE P.O.W.

BAT MORGAN

- CONFEDERATE REBEL
- BUFFALO HIDE HUNTER

VASHTI EPPS

- GUN MOLL
- CATTLE BARONESS

UTOKA JETT

- MADAM
- UNDERCOVER AGENT

PELHAM WARE

- VAGABOND DETECTIVE

Introduction

The book, "Tales of the Undaunted," is composed of a collection of fictional events (based to a large extent on facts) that have gained legendary status due to their historical significance, tales of episodic adventures and valor on the battlefield of the wilderness; tales of men like Josh Epps, the mountain man, wagoneer, and guide for wagon trains, blazing trails across the uncharted frontier of the west; of drovers and cattle barons cutting a thrilling and dangerous path through hostile natives, and stories of the valiant ranging men (Texas Rangers) pursuing the lawless and the renegade Comanches, (Lords of the plains), making safe the 1300 mile frontier of western Texas.

There are numerous accounts of undaunted courage displayed by the life and times of the pioneers, early Americans. They came to North America to carve out a life, burrowing themselves in the wilderness, isolated, to escape poverty, people of different nationalities, of diverse society, unable to communicate due to language barriers, people who had developed the ability to disregard fear, brave and valiant, eager to share the common knowledge existing about life in America. Decades passed and these people, undaunted, burrowed deeper in isolation. Wagoneers, beating their sweating teams over mountains, across streams, through mud holes and burning prairies played a large part in rescuing the venturers from isolation. Along with this element came the itinerate tellers of the tall tales. They spawned a form of cultural literacy that formed the basis of social, cultural, and religious events that bonded families whom heretofore were strangers. The talented teller of the tall tales were celebrants; people brought their children to listen; the gathering and events generated understanding of matters that eventually became common knowledge far and wide. Throughout the vast American frontier this form of cultural literacy bonded America into a formidable force. To a large extent this common knowledge spurred by the tales of the undaunted, became a collective memory that allowed this conglomerate of people to communicate and to work together and to live together. These memories passed from generation to generation created a permanent place in America's cultural heritage.

The characters in the "Tales of The Undaunted," exposed to the ravages of their environment, and to the constant peril of the untamed wilderness, existing in loneliness, depicted a country of people where staying alive was an achievement.

THE UNDAUNTED

Mountain Man

Chapter One

THE MOUNTAIN MAN

Josh Epps was born in the year 1800, in the coalmining village of Pocahontas, Virginia. At age 20 he had grown into a striking figure, tall and handsome. His 6'3", 180-pound frame was lithe and quick. His long arms and huge hands reached almost to his knees. His hair, raven black, shaggy and uncut, his face was clean shaven except for a bristly mustache and bulging side burns.

At age 20, Josh was basically illiterate. He was lazy and avoided work and school. He eventually learned to read and write, but his spelling was an exercise in originality. He was jovial, fun loving, and mischievous. For fun times he engaged in street wrestling, much to the disgust of his parents and this behavior led to being banished from their small cabin. Josh was undaunted and quickly responded to his innate sense of adventure. He went to Missouri where he signed on with a party of "fur trappers." This venture signaled the beginning of his life as a mountain man. He quickly found this life style and the environment much to his liking. He admired the trappers' rugged adventurous attitude, and he fell into immediate acceptance. His associates were truly men of peril.

ASIDE:

Mountain men roamed the Rocky Mountain region in search of the valuable fur of animals, especially the beaver, during the first half of the 19th century. Although motivated by the desire for personal gain, they established trade and accumulated information that added greatly to the settlements of the western frontier. The hay day of the mountain man began with William Henry Ashley and Andrew Henry's expedition of the upper Missouri River in 1822. During the next 18 years, American, French and Spanish trappers discovered passes through the Rocky Mountains, explored the great basin and far southwest, and developed several useful routes to California and Oregon. During the time of Josh Epp's career as a mountain man, perhaps as many as 3000 mountain men operated in the far west. Some worked for fur companies. Some, like Josh, worked independently, known as "free trappers." They sold their furs to the highest bidder at the summer rendezvous held annually from 1825 to 1840. Despite their wild reputations, many mountain men were well educated, but not Josh Epps; however he proved to be shrewd in business dealings.

The mountain man lived in isolation for much of the year. They adopted the way of life of the Indian, in order to survive the dangers of the wilderness. They were an *undaunted breed.*

In 1840 the fur trade dwindled and some mountain men returned to civilization, whereas others stayed in the west, as did Josh, and became much sought after as guides and Indian scouts for wagon trains, cattle drovers, and lawmen.

Living in isolation, year after year and in constant peril, gave rise to the development of certain characteristics of the mountain man. Most all trappers assembled at rendezvous bringing their furs and taking new supplies of clothing, ammunition and goods for trade with the Indians. But few of these men ever returned to their country and friends. Most of them were constantly in debt to the company and were unwilling to retire without a fortune; and year after year passed away while they were hoping in vain for better success.

When the mountain men assembled at a rendezvous, it was another day of indulgence, in which all restraint was laid aside. These days were the climax of a hunter's happiness. Their toils and privations were so great that they more readily compensated themselves by plunging into such excesses, as in their mistaken judgment of things seemed most adapted to give them pleasures.

A particular characteristic of the mountain men is they divided the common place phrases of profanity which prevail among the impious vulgar in civilized countries, and have many set phrases which they appear to have manufactured among themselves, and which they bring into almost every sentence and on all occasions. By varying the tone of their voices they make them expressions of joy, hope, grief, and anger. In their homes among themselves, which did not happen every day, they are not ungenerous. They would see "fair play" and "spare the last eye," and would not tolerate murder unless drunken or great provocation could be placed in extenuation.

Their demoralizing influence with Indians was limiting and they practiced impositions upon them in all the ways that sinful propensity dictated. It is said that they told them if they refused to give the mountain man wives that the Gods would be angry with them and punish them eternally. Maybe this was true, but actually their wishes were accomplished largely by flattery and presents, for most of them squandered away their wages for their women and children.

Josh's good humor and ability to reel off an inexhaustible string of tall tales found favor with his crude companions. Josh's melodious voice and backwoods drawl held people spellbound. His range of exploits substantiated his towering reputation as a gifted storyteller. He relished telling how he killed a she-grizzly with his bare hands, and had scars to prove it. He would describe in rich detail his hand-to-paw battle with the grizzly that cuffed him several times before he sunk his tomahawk into her brains. He also had fought the red warriors who resented the mountain man's invasion of their homelands. He told of an encounter with a Black Feet Warrior when he was nearly killed. The warrior drew his bow while Josh was reloading his Hawken rifle, but the Black Feet's bow was strung too tight, causing the arrow to drop to the ground which gave Josh time for a fatal shot.

Josh and his trapper associates lived a life of continued exertions, peril and excitement. They were men enamored by their occupation: No toil, no danger, no privation could turn a trapper from his pursuit. His passionate excitement resembled a maniac's. In vain may the most vigilant and cruel savage beset his path; or win-frey torrent, oppose his progress when a single track of a Beaver met his eye and he forgets all danger and defies all difficulties.

Josh soon found the trappers were genuine mountain men from whom he could learn much, thus fortifying his chance for survival. Many had descended from immigrants, who came to America in the early 1700's. They were toughened by the grim warfare of the Scottish lowlands and accustomed to the cutthroat troubles of Ireland, and were very much at home with Indian fighting in America. They made the best possible frontiersman. They got their education from the ways of the forest and passed it along to posterity. They could trap animals, avoid poison ivy, bees and wasps; identify sounds, build a fire in the rain, and fell trees across a stream to make a bridge.

Josh fitted right in with the life style of the "free trappers." His huge physique, and catlike movement, resulting from years of street wrestling, made him an imposing member of the group.

There was much for Josh to learn about the trapping industry, the fur trade, and the rendezvous system of marketing, as well as history of the early American prospectors.

The first settlers prospected for gold but found that furs were a good substitute. Furs could be sold for gold. The wealthy in Europe, as well as later in America, wanted fur garments.

Ownership was a status symbol of their social standing. Explorers reported the Rocky Mountains swarmed with fur bearing animals. Venturesome men hastened after their pelts. Big expeditions were sent up from Missouri in the early 1800's. Thereafter each year, companies departed St. Louis to spend a year or more in the mountains, trapping for pelts. Successful expeditions made fortunes, while a bad season, or an over turned keelboat on return trips would turn a years hard work into nothing.

Josh and his group of venturers participated in a number of expeditions deep into the mountains, trusting to luck and praying for a safe return.

The men who managed the fur trade devised the "rendezvous system" of marketing. They set a time and place a year in advance, where their own pack train, as well as the "free trappers" would meet the exchange and trade goods for the year's catch of furs.

On his first rendezvous, Josh was awed by the appearance of the gathering. The camping place was several long rows of Indian lodges (tepees) extending along a river for almost two miles. Indians and whites were mingled in various groups. Josh discovered the tribes consisted mostly of Snakes, Flatheads, and Navajos, all peaceful tribes. The whites were agents of different trading companies and a quantity of trappers who had found their way there. While visiting this "fair in the wilderness" they would buy and sell, and renew old contracts and make new ones: They would make arrangements for future meetings, meet old friends, tell tall tales, and spend for once a jolly day.

These trappers, known as "knights, without fear and without reproach" were a peculiar set of people, so much so it is necessary to say a little about them.

The mountain men (knights) either received their outfit, consisting of horses, beaver traps, gunpowder and lead, from a trading company, trapping for small wages, or else they acted on their own account and were known as "freemen". This was Josh's case. He was a part of a small party who roamed through all the mountain passes. No rock was too steep for them; no stream too swift. They lived in constant danger from hostile Indians whose delight was to ambush small parties, plunder them, and scalp them. However, this audacious daily danger seemed to exercise a magic attraction over Josh. Only with extreme reluctance would he abandon his dangerous craft.

In manners and customs, the mountain men borrowed much from the Indians. Many of them took Indian women for wives. Clothing was leather, and they wore their hair long. In place of money, they used beaver skins for which they were able to supply all their needs, by way of trading.

At the yearly rendezvous the trappers sought to indemnify themselves for the suffering and privations for a year spent in the wilderness. With hairy bank notes, the beaver skins, they could obtain all the luxuries of the mountains, and live for a few days like Lords. Coffee and chocolate was cooked; the pipe kept aglow day and night; the spirits circulated; and whatever was not spent in such ways, the squaws coaxed out of them, or else it was squandered at cards. Single trappers often wasted up to a thousand dollars.

Over the years, attending successive rendezvous, Josh observed the glory days were fading away. It was sad. Constant hunting had reduced the number of beaver. Each year the diminution in the beaver catch was noticeable. The last year of Josh's attendance, the behavior of the trappers was quieter; there was little drinking of spirits, and almost no gambling. Josh predicted that within another decade the original trapper will disappear from the mountains.

A rendezvous usually lasted a full week, and then the different parties moved off to their destination. The plains, that one day resounded with barbarous music, and was thronged with people of both races with their horses and dogs, returns to its old quiet, interrupted only now and then by the muffled roar of the buffalo and the howl of the wolf.

Even as Josh witnessed the on-coming demise of the "wilderness fair," he felt but little regrets. It was not all that big a deal for him. He engaged in limited games and entertainment. His forte was bargaining for profits. Josh, like most other mountain men, did not relish seeing their year of hard work slipping through their fingers at gaming tables, horseracing, foot races and wrestling matches. Nor did he seek favors of the squaws who consistently pursued the trapper to gain access to their beaver pelts. In fact, after about three days of attendance, Josh preferred returning to the wilderness and the quiet solitude of the nights.

Josh was a shrewd trader. A pound of beaver skins was paid for with four dollars worth of goods, but the goods were sold at enormous prices, so called mountain prices. A pint of meal cost from a half to one dollar; a pint of coffee beans, cocoa beans, or sugar two dollars each; a pint of diluted alcohol four dollars; a piece of chewing tobacco one to two dollars. Guns, ammunition, bear traps, blankets, kerchiefs, and gaudy finery for the squaws also sold at enormous profits.

Josh's sense of entrepreneurship opened an avenue for some astute trading. After one or two rendezvous he learned which goods would go the fastest and be in most demand during the final days of the "fair." He traded and bartered for these "demand goods" and hoarded them until the time was right to expose them for sale. Then he hit a windfall of profits. Being somewhat selfish and stingy, he hoarded his money by squirreling it away in a secret cache, which he located during his first days in attendance. Thieves and robbers were prevalent in the wilderness, as well as the Indians, all looking for an easy take. Earning and conniving to gain dollars at the rendezvous was only a small part of the venture. The big part was getting safely away with it. Josh's jovial and carefree nature, coupled with his towering physique, camouflaged him as a possessor of wealth. He also found that it was important to find favor with the Indians as further protection from a personal raid or attack.

To the rendezvous the Indians came by the thousands. They were no less interesting than the trappers. Their tents were made of buffalo hides, tanned on both sides and sewed together and stretched in cone shapes over a dozen poles that leaned against each other, tops crossing. In front, and on top, this leather could be thrown back forming a door and chimney. Tents were about 12 feet high and 20 feet in circumference at the ground. The tents gave sufficient protection from the weather. Josh visited many of these tents to barter for trifles and to make himself more intelligible in the language and signs. An army of Indian dogs usually beset the entrance. The Indians had for trade chiefly tanned buffalo hair and fresh or dried buffalo meat. They had no beaver skins. The articles that attracted the most in exchange were powder and lead, knives, tobacco, and gaily colored kerchiefs, pocket mirrors, and all sorts of ornaments.

In a rare foray, Josh challenged a young chief to a wrestling match. There was substantial betting; all instigated by the young chief's father and other members of the family. He was a handsome young man, with a hourglass figure and washboard belly. He was stripped to the waist and strutted before his admirers in grandiose fashion. The trappers and others in the clearing were awed by this physical specimen. The betting became more intense when the old chief led into the makeshift arena a great roan gelding. The most handsome horse Josh had ever seen. The bet between the two adversaries was the chief's horse against Josh's gun, pack mule and fringed buckskin coat. Josh could ill afford to lose, and had no intention of doing so. His heart skipped a beat when confronted by the lithe young chief, but he wanted that great roan badly.

Josh appeared rather awkwardly as he walked into the arena. He had a feeling the crowd was already feeling sorry for him. Then he straightened from his slouched position, threw off his buckskin shirt, tossed about his shoulders the long raven tresses, and flexed his sinewy muscle. He was a virtual picture of a strapping, sturdy, brawny muscular being, tough, vigorous and robust. He saw the startled look on the young chief's face as he moved cat-like around the ring. The crowd lapped into dead silence as they envisioned their bets vanishing under the clash that was about to occur. At the first contact Josh quickly maneuvered his body into position to pick-up the Indian bodily and swirling him once overhead slammed him to the ground. The crowd moaned. Josh sprawled on the opponent and the match was over. The old chief led the great gelding into the ring, handed the tether to his young son, and grimly said, "give him—you lost badly." Josh felt badly for the young man but then he surmised if he had been on the receiving end the crowd would have had no sympathy. He smiled at the crowd, patted the young chief on the shoulder, and led his prize away.

As Josh departed the site of his last rendezvous he paused momentarily and looked back down the trail he had just traversed. It would soon be daybreak and the bustle of activity would commence. He purposefully left before daybreak to conceal his direction to the cache, which was a full day away from the camp, avoiding detection while retrieving his money required much caution. The great roan was now loaded like a pack animal, carrying camp and hunting gear. His own horse, Star, appeared to enjoy the company of another horse, as he had an obvious disdain for the contrary pack mule. Josh smiled and openly apologized to the roan: "you are too beautiful and majestic to be lowered to the status of a pack mule. Along the way we will find reason to change this." They traveled all day and located the cache late afternoon, a small opening to a large hollow in a branch of a gum tree. Josh made camp.

During the night, Josh squirmed and rolled in his bag. This was unusual for Josh, and the livestock nervously moved about. The thoughts of no more rendezvous fluttered through his mind. Obviously, the trapping industry was fading out as a means of livelihood for men of the mountains. What's next, and where to from here? Go home to the coalmines, definitely not! It would be good to see his parents! Would they want to see him? He was very much in disfavor eight years ago when they literally ran him off. Can't blame them, he was a 20 year old good for nothing brat. But what they did to him was the greatest gift they could have ever given. He was bewildered but undaunted.

Home life was no walk in the park! He was born in poverty. His parents had come to America to escape poverty. They, too, had been born into poverty, which Josh supposed, was the norm in human history. These circumstances, by normal expectations, endangered his life to become conditioned to look at life in a negative way. That whatever he was to get out of life he would get last. However, why he did not know, he never grew up with the feeling the "short end of the stick" had his name on it. All his adolescent life he perceived it did not have to be that way. When he was banished from the little cabin, too small for three people and especially his lazy hulk. . . He perceived he had two choices: whether life in the untamed wilderness awaited him with laughter and good times, or with angered frustration. Whether he would spend his life in bitterness and disappointment, complaining about what he did not have, or make the hardships vanish and cherish what he did have. The wilderness had a way of bringing the best out of men and Josh had been privileged to meet the challenge.

As to his future, Josh surmised the whole frontier would become an extension of life of the past eight years. Adventure abounded in any and all directions. The thought of adventure under a change in circumstances would be something to pursue. The western frontier intrigued him; Texas, the wild cattle, the free land, he had heard about. Something to think about, he mused.

Shortly after daybreak he broke camp and prepared to move on. Star was anxious to travel, the big roan was docile and obedient; the pack mule was belligerent and constantly rubbing against canyon walls, and trees to dislodge his pack. Josh discovered a mountain trail leading to a cove. He glimpsed a small-enclosed lake at the end of a bridal waterfall, a good place to take on a supply of fresh water. As he descended the trail into full view of the pond he could hear the waterfall flowing over the rocky cliff above the pristine pool. Both horses nickered, nostrils flared and ears sharply pricked. Star nervously pulled at Josh. Above the ledge, there cavorted two black bear cubs. Below the ledge under the waterfall, stood a beautiful Indian maiden, in the nude, casually brushing her long black hair. There before Josh stood the most beautiful female body he had ever seen. But his heart pounded with apprehension; he immediately assessed the situation as fraught with danger. The she-bear had to be close by, keeping an eye on her cubs. Holding tightly to the horses, he quickly snubbed them to a tree and moved closer to the pond. By the configuration of the pool, the waterfall and the ledge, the girl must be between the cubs and their mother. This could be a disaster. The girl had now placed a blanket underneath a willow tree and lay prone facing the sun. The cubs were out of her view, but plainly in Josh's. Then it happened, the she-bear spotted the girl and growled deeply, slowly approaching the opposite bank of the pool. The Indian maiden leaped to her feet, swinging the blanket in an effort to frighten the bear away. Josh knew this wouldn't work. The bear was there to protect her cubs.

The girl became frightened and screamed at the bear. She was hemmed in. As the bear reared to her hind legs for a plunge across the pond, Josh acted. He sprang from behind a small thicket and charged the bear from the rear. He grasped the startled animal around the neck, with his left hand he took her full lower jaw, wrenching the head to his left and driving his long knife to her chest. It was not lethal. Her strong forelegs and paw knocked him to the ground. Josh charged upward with his tomahawk, slashing away part of her face, and now it was a paw to hand battle. Claws tore at Josh's buckskin shirt, ripping away flesh. He lunged, throwing the bear off balance, and she retaliated by charging on all fours. Josh sunk the tomahawk into her brain and the grizzly fell still at his feet.

Witnessing the conflict between man and animal, the girl dashed across the pond scantily clad, dragging her cloth palette through the water. The exhausted, mountain man lay sprawled and bleeding. She quickly dabbed at his gaping wounds, pressing the wet palette hard against the flow of blood. The two "orphaned" cubs scampered into the woods.

Josh lay still, his head in her lap, and gazed into her radiant eyes, exuding pools of pain, gratitude, and admiration for this young giant of the wilderness. A cool morning breeze further enhanced the cloth, which was repeatedly dipped into the cool waters of the pristine pool, and applied to his throbbing body. The soothing effect of the emergency aid was excelled only by the maiden's exquisite beauty. Josh experienced a strange thrill surging through his body, sensual and emotional. To experience this comfort makes it all worthwhile. Soon they reached a nearby tribal village of Shawnees. Her father, the chief, listened silently to the rescue of his princess daughter.

Two days later, Josh prepared for departure. He made a gift of the grizzly's hide to the old chief who thanked him profusely. Josh reluctantly bade farewell, mounted his horse, Star, and leading the roan and the pack mule turned away. But he was stopped. The beautiful princess held Star's bridal and smiled at Josh. Startled, Josh stared at this vision of loveliness feeling he was seeing her for the last time. She spoke, "father say me go be your wife." The flutter of Josh's heart almost unseated him. He looked at her father puzzled. "You take, you good man, she good girl, make you good wife," spoke the Chief. Tears welled in the old chief's eyes. Josh leaped from Star and with great joy, picked up the princess and boldly planted her astride Star. She looked down tearfully at her father, then turned to Josh and smiled. Josh was on fire. He quickly mounted the roan and they departed.

The trail was harsh and tedious. The pack mule was a constant problem, objecting to his increased load now that the roan had been relieved of his pack and taken on Josh. The roan was pleased but the mule fought back showing his displeasure. "If you don't behave, I'm going to run you over the cliff, pack and all," Josh admonished. The princess giggled and kept her eyes on Josh constantly. What a lucky girl I am, she thought. Funny he doesn't even know my name. But then,

I don't know his. To Josh, she was a vision of loveliness, sitting majestically astride Star who pranced along the trail as if carrying royalty.

High noon found them beside a small brook that tumbled down the mountain side, kicking up white water as it challenged the small boulders in its course. Cold and clean, they all drank deeply. Josh loosened the girt on Star and lifted away the saddle and pack. "Good place to rest, many hours to Trappers Cove where we will spend the night." He spread a blanket for the alluring princess. She stretched herself before him with no intention to tantalize him, and Josh, flustered by her shapely body, sat down beside her. Her adoring eyes melted his heart. His chest began to throb. He muttered like a scared kid and breathlessly remarked, "me Josh," and she said "me Willow by the Spring."

It was late in the evening when Josh and Willow pulled up at the hitching rail of the local tavern. "Trappers Cove" was a small settlement on the Missouri River, known more as a dispersing point for venturesome settlers, trappers, hunters, Indian fighters, guides, and other frontier occupations. This was the gathering point and the last spot in civilization before stepping off and burrowing deep in the wilderness, isolated. To keep abreast of what was going on in the New World depended upon how frequently one came in contact with a man of stories, celebrants who ranged the frontier, the tellers of tall tales. From these men, settlers learned customs and systems, formulated communities, how to communicate with each other, and even laugh at each other's jokes. Trappers Cove was a haven for this strange breed of pioneers. They were somewhat akin to itinerant men of the cloth who followed, and sometimes preceded settlers into the wilderness. These individuals attained legendary status by their ability to embellish events with great exaggeration. They mastered the art of presentation. Having a good story was one thing, but unless it was sung right it was ineffective. Into Trappers Cove people brought their children to listen whenever word that a teller of tall tales was in the area. Parents learned that the stories, embellished as they were, usually were wrapped in meaningful lessons of the day. These gatherings formed a basis of social culture and religious events, and bonded families whom heretofore were strangers. The events generated understandings of affairs that eventually became common knowledge throughout the vast American frontier.

Josh fitted well into the art of these storytellers. No one was more accomplished than Josh. His giant imposing physique, deep laughter, backwoods drawl, found favor with both men and women and he could reel off an inexhaustible string of tall tales in an artful fashion. He and Willow found the cove to be a welcomed break from the rigors of the wilderness and they made the most of their stay, cooped up in a small room. The "flat," as the brothel was known, was not a decent place to be living with a beautiful bride, and Josh realized he was courting danger. The place was rife with lawless, prostitutes, gunman, deadbeats, and hoodlums. They looked upon Indians as savages, and upon their women as pawns to be used for pleasure at will. Willow by the Spring was terribly in peril for abuse. Josh's sense of protection and good judgment dictated "get out promptly." He would do so without delay; tomorrow for sure, but too late. Josh and Willow took their seat at a customary table in back of the saloon (brothel), to order their evening meal. Three men, unsavory characters, to say the least, approached them. One invited Josh to join them at a gaming table for cards, ignoring Willow. He politely declined. Then one responded with a snarl "he'd rather be in bed with that squaw than have a good time with some decent people." Swift as a cat, Josh smashed his powerful fist in the man's face, and he went down and out as if hit by a poll-axe. Another jumped into the fray and received identical crushing blows, Josh's arms working like a jackhammer. The third man struck Josh over the head and shoulder with a chair, which Josh brushed deftly aside. He picked the man up bodily and threw him across two tables where he lay still joining his two cronies.

Josh sat with Willow, breathing heavily. She sat silently with wider eyes of admiration for her handsome mountain man. He smiled appreciatively and said, "I need a drink." He walked to the bar and ordered whisky.

A tall frontiersman was standing at the bar, dressed in buckskins from head to foot. He was every bit as large as Josh and Josh could not help but notice the congenial expression on his face. Josh sized him up immediately as not the run of the mill type who frequented the flat.

"Must be some squaw to put up a fight like you just did," he smiled. Josh replied congenially "ain't no squaw, she's my wife." "That figures, you two do make an imposing pair," he remarked. "Name's Sam Dale, General Sam Dale." They shook hands. "I'm Josh Epps, just plain Josh a mountain man and trapper."

General Dale joined Josh and Willow for supper and more drinks. They talked well into the evening. Willow excused herself and went to her room.

"What I'm saying, Josh. Being a wagon train guide, my route takes me across country endangered by marauding Indians, and every type of lawless hoodlum you can name. I contract to get these people to their destination and safely. They are largely, families who don't mind long days, traveling hardships, and provocation. But they're not good at fighting and warding off raids. I need help. Putting it bluntly I need you." With that said Sam leaned back in his chair and fired up a battered cigar.

Josh was silent for several minutes. Sam understood. Racing through Josh's mind was his future. His trapping days were over, he was sure; he had no other profession but fighting Indians and pounding the dangerous frontier. He had known nothing but peril and danger all his life. Adventure was in his soul. He had no alternative but to pursue it. But, what about Willow? They loved each other though together only a few days. He cringed at the thought of giving her up.

Sam apparently read Josh's mind. "No big hurry for a decision, make plans for your lovely wife and meet me at Cades

Cove in Gatlinburg, Tennessee six months from now. I am rendezvousing there at that time, putting the train together and moving out for Mississippi. "We are gonna have a war and Mississippi will be right in the middle of it. I want to get in and get out before it heats up; lot of trouble between the North and the South." Sam walked away leaving Josh to decide his fate, his future, and his life. Josh turned in. He would talk to Willow tomorrow. Wagon trains, marauding Indians, adventurous settlers, western frontier, millions of wild cattle, free land. Josh's adventuresome spirit was being challenged. He longed to be a part of the vast movement of Americans westward, but first things first. Willow, Willow, Willow . . . , she danced wistfully before his wide-awake eyes. She comes first, and he feels remorse that he would have to leave her so soon. The future was too fraught with danger to give any thought to taking her on his proposed journey. He sighed deeply, and fell into a deep sleep.

Josh fully intended covering with Willow the discussion with Sam Dale first thing next morning. When he rose he lapsed into complete reluctance to do so. No need to spawn unhappiness at this time.

Willow was radiant on this clear day in the mountains. Josh had a jolly attitude, but she suspicioned he was hiding something from her. She perceived the meeting between Sam Dale and Josh forbade an unpleasant future. Regardless of the outcome of the meeting, she was determined to support her handsome mountain man and love.

TEAMSTER BEATING HIS TEAM OVER THE MOUNTAINS AND THRU MUD HOLES, ETC. PILED HIGH LOAD—ETC.

Chapter Two

THE WAGONEERS

On a frosty November morning, Josh made contact with a teamster of recognition, Brent Wilson. He found Wilson holding camp in one of his own wagons. A typical live alone wagoneer. He spoke, "let me tell you what you are getting into, Mr. Epps. First, you will be dealing with a different kind of animal than the usual horse and mule. These horses are dray horses of the Belgium and Clydesdale species. They weigh over one ton each, and they can move a mountain. Secondly, you won't be driving down a well-traveled and defined road. You will be following a trail left by someone else; or you'll make your own trails by guessing, cussing, and praying. You will be delivering stuff to crazy people who have burrowed themselves so deep in the wilderness they are completely isolated. They pay well to receive a wagonload of supplies and merchandise. We have to pile it high, and dangerously positioned. I don't expect you to lose a load, or lose your way."

Having said that, he put the end of a burning ember to his pipe and puffed. From under the brim of his beaver hat he peered at Josh to observe his reaction. Josh replied, "when do I get my first load out?"

Brent Wilson had started his hauling business years ago. He was the first man to bring merchandise to the southern route. He drove four Belgiums with a load weighing 2000 pounds, for which he was paid three dollars per hundred. It took almost a month to make the trip from Hagerstown, to Brownsville. A distance of 140 miles, Brent practically blazed the road for the trip. Later, however, with road improvements, he used six horses, hitched in tandem, and hauled 70,000 to 80,000 pounds for which he received one dollar per hundred. He now made the trip in seven days. He became financially affluent in the business and expanded his venture. Josh was one of the first to take on Wilson's expanded enterprise.

ASIDE:

The westward movement was slowed by the lack of a system of roads, and trails. Those who braved the uncertain journey westward found the going too dire and disheartening, and the distance great. Travel involved, not only hazard to personal comfort, but life as well. Along the way of most any route or trail that allowed travel, were at best the most meager accommodations. Taverns were insect ridden and dirty. Most land routes, which penetrated the frontier before 1800 were developed from trails; which were connected to landmarks in the wilderness. They usually led to salt licks, and good grazing grounds, and sought out mountain passes and fording places across bigger streams. They were seldom blazed and rarely improved; always over-hanging limbs and rockslides obstructed them. Animals and Wagoneer's alike went around obstacles as they developed. A legend exists that east of the Mississippi, the buffalo always found the easiest grade and made the safest crossing of streams. Even the buffalo trails, after discovery, often became completely obliterated by the growth of vegetation. Yet it was along such trails that frontiersman broke the way into the western country.

Josh soon found that the wagon teamsters were a special breed of Americans. They beat and thundered their way over the hills and out of mud-holes. Their sweating teams strained to deliver towering loads of textiles, farm implements, salt, tools, furniture, seafood, Yankee notions, and merchandise of all sorts to their western destinations. Private and public freight wagons bulged with household goods of settlers on their way to a new country. Piles of fur skins, hemp, whiskey, cured meats, potash, and tobacco went west. Thousands of bushels of corn and wheat and endless barrels of flour sought passage to the market. Wagon yards were crowded with rowdy drivers. Josh melded right in and became one of them. A past time was spinning yarns of road adventures, and bragging of their romances along the way with tavern scullions and the female contingent of settler's caravans.

Josh soon found that loading up and hitting the road with 2-ton horses was only a part of the Wagoneer's career. The other part was staying alive, which was an achievement in itself. Traversing the early roads pushing thru the wilderness, rescuing settlers from isolation was marred by blood shed and plundering. While the highway bandits robbed only a small number of travelers, the account of their heartless banditry survived even the road itself.

Josh soon became disenchanted with the ugly profession of Wagoneer. He was lonesome for Willow. He hastened to shake loose from his contract with Brent Wilson, pick-up Willow, and move on. Move on? To where? The thought plagued him. Josh could not make the decision for their future alone; he would seek input from Willow. His last trip had taken him away for several weeks, as was typical, of wagoneering.

Willow cuddled close to her man of the mountains. They talked well into the evening snuggling under warm blankets; Willow giggled playfully, and moved Josh's huge hand to her lower abdomen. "Feel anything?" she giggled. "Can't say as I do, what are you getting at?" "We are having a little papoose," she laughed heartily. "Aren't you thrilled and happy?" Josh swallowed hard, this changes things, drastically he thought to himself.

A baby! Josh was too apprehensive of Willow's welfare to feel the thrill of parenthood. Our whole future is impaired. What about the wagon train job? Josh was thrilled beyond comprehension at the thought of this new adventure. He had not promised Dale he would hire on, but he felt all along he could not resist. Too, the six months rendezvous date at Cades Cove was only a few weeks away. A decision had to be made, more than one—what's best for Willow and the birthplace of the baby, and his association with Sam Dale.

Willow gazed long and deep into Josh's eyes. She was sensitive to the thoughts racing through his mind and heart. They both recognized that the predicament at hand must be fully comprehended, grasped, and dealt with. Neither wanted to speak out and break this blissful awareness, fearing the decision that was inescapable; a bitter and decisive direction confronted their well-being, their life.

After a full week of negotiating infrequently used mountain trails, crossing streams, scaling canyons and warding off insects, bees and wasps, they arrived at her parents, Shawnee Village. Josh had been warned about the fierce nature of any tribe belonging to the Algonquin Nation, such as the Shawnee's. They were an organized league of cutthroats, raiders, and vicious savages. The Iroquois-speaking nation was intensely committed to warfare and taking captives, and with torture and cannibalism inflicted on male captives. Josh's initial contact had been pleasant enough, but the circumstances had been different. Willow had been rescued from an angry grizzly; he was wounded and had made a gift to the chief. In turn the Father reciprocated with a gift of a wife. Now that gift was heavy with child and he was returning her to her family. He was a bit apprehensive as to how this is going to go over. He was told by frontiersman in the know, "one thing to avoid is a member of the Iroquois, Shawnee, Cayuga, Mohawk Onondaga, Oneida, and Seneca tribes." Willow was a Shawnee. The Iroquois were known to practice cannibalism, torturing captive male notables, cutting out their genitals, and devouring them.

It was dusk when they reached the village; they had ridden hard to make their destination before dark. Tired and weary, Willow dismounted gently from Star and into Josh's arms. Other than a pack of barking dogs they were greeted with solemnity from the women, and with a stoical expression from her Father and two young braves standing nearby. I don't think we are welcome, thought Josh. Then he preceded to tell the chief and Willow's mother, her two brothers, that Willow was heavy with child and he was called away where Willow could not go; they begged permission for Willow to birth her child with her mother's help and for the Chief to maintain and care for Willow and child, while many moons later Josh would return and get his family together again. This didn't go over so well and the indications on the sullen faces of Willow's family were not acceptable. Numerous grunts, and indistinguishable words were exchanged among Willow's family, resulting in expressions of apprehension and alarm on Willow's countenance. She attacked her father, beating him with her clenched fist, shouting no, no he good man. With one swoop of his arm the chief motioned her away. The two brothers picked Willow up bodily and took her away. Josh's spasmodic response crashed the two Shawnees from the rear, and jerked Willow loose. What Josh had not observed was a third Shawnee observing this action from a shadow, and with a cat-like leap slugged Josh in the head and he went down and out.

Josh regained his consciousness some time during the night. It was eerie quiet. He opened his eyes and saw the starry sky above. He attempted to sit, but could not budge from the ground. Both hands were pinned down by stakes, and legs stretched apart with both feet staked down. A Shawnee torture pose, known throughout the Iroquois Nation as normal practice applied to any notable white male who fell victim to their savagery. The Shawnees made a ceremony of it. They referred to it as the Red Warriors deterrent to the White mans invasion of their land. Josh was more than just perturbed, he was literally terrified. They would treat Willow in this manner and persecute him likewise, in contrast to the sincere-like, expression of appreciation for Josh having saved Willow's life from the she- grizzly. Sincerity faked, a trait of the red man.

Josh applied his great strength to loosen himself. After incessant straining at the stakes he sensed a slight release from their base. Encouraged, he continued intermittent surges of yanks at the stakes binding his hands. He had to hurry. Dawn was at hand, and he realized his torturers would be there by sunrise. One stake came loose, he quickly turned to the other and with mighty strength he pulled the other from the ground. Quickly he pulled at the buckskin thongs to unbind his hands; then he unbound his feet, but left the binding loosely around the ankles. He did likewise to his hands and wrist then shoved the stakes back in the holes. He resumed his tied down position. It was daybreak and he could see the dogs nosing around the teepees, and heard muffled voices. He spotted a female going into a tent with a pale of water. She came out empty handed. Willow: this is where they are holding Willow. He waited. They came, three stalwart braves. They grunted and motioned to each other, and then two walked away. The third, grinning like an idiot, pulled his long knife, proudly ran his thumb along the razor-like edge. Then slit open Josh's buckskin pants at the crouch. Obviously, it was the Shawnees intent to castrate him and deliver his testicles to the presiding chief. They would make big medicine of this while stringing him up by the heels and let him bleed to death.

The grinning warrior knelt to perform the laceration. Josh came down on him with both his powerful arms, grabbed the long knife and with one big swipe almost decapited the Indian. It was over quickly, and Josh moved swiftly to Willow's tent.

Willow startled, was curled on the floor of the teepee, hands and feet bound with a pale of water nearby. Josh cut loose her bindings, slit the rear of the tent and they slithered into the underbrush, and melted into the wilderness. Hours later they paused by a small stream and drank. Then they sat by a tree trunk for some much needed rest. "Can't stay here long, by now they have a party out for us, I don't think your family likes us," Josh said.

Over one month later, after escaping from the wilderness, by foot, horseback and wagon, they made it to the little village of Pocahontas. Willow had a very prominent bulge below the waistline. Her eyes were deep set and hallow. Josh feared for her health. Surely we will not receive the kind of reception we went through with her parents, thought Josh.

They located the old home place. No change except older and more dilapidated. The setting was awesome. His thoughts, bounded back to his days when he could leap from the broken down porch to the ground holding his small wistful mother in his arms. She would scold him for his ridiculous behavior, and he would laugh. A sense of awe surged thru his heart. The place is too solemn to be real. "They ain't here," he blurted out.

Josh mounted the rickety steps to the weather-beaten creaky porch. A screen door closed on the doorway, the lower part half torn away. He peered inside. He thought he could make out the figure of a person. The room was dim. Then a deep guttural voice; "come in Josh." This voice was not his dad's but who else could have recognized him after a full ten years absence? "I recognized you when you came on the yard. Who's the woman?" Josh recovered from the astonishment and stammered, "she's my wife, who are you?" "Name's Doc Purdy, longtime friend of your maw and paw." "Where's maw and paw, this is where they lived ten years ago?" "Lot's happened in ten years Josh." Then Doc Purdy proceeded to tell a heart-rending story of Josh's parents. "Your pa died neigh on to six years ago with the black lung, just like all us miners will go," Doc said. "Your maw lived alone here, or I might say existed here for another three years. We all pitched in and helped her with food and stuff. She was so unhappy. Always asking, "when is Josh coming home?" His voice quivered. "Was bad Josh, was a blessing to see her go." Josh was doing his best to control his heaving heart. He thought surely it would burst.

He was a hard crusted man of the mountains, but he had emotions, and feelings like every decent human. His thoughts turned inward. Here I was, a selfish person roaming around the mountains, having a mix of times, the quality of which some good some bad, but unmindful of the needs of my mother. Indeed he thought, I forgot I had a mother. She was so adamant about my leaving, guess I assumed that was the end of our relationship. But mother and son do not sever relationships regardless of the circumstances. I realize that now, but too late, murmured Josh. "You live alone?" "Nope, wives out back digging in the garden, be in shortly." Willow spoke for the first time, "she do all the work, like women of my people?" Doc turned and looked at Willow as if suddenly discovering her presence. "Woman you must be Indian," he said bluntly. Willow smiled wanly.

Pearl Purdy hustled thru the back door breathing heavily, while carrying a basket of fresh vegetables. "Whose this?" she demanded, sternly as if being invaded. "Sug (short for sugar) this is the Epps's boy, Josh and wife." "Lands sake, I'd of never knowed it, how you have aged. Must've been gone 5 or 6 years." "Ten years, Mam," Josh replied. "Then no wonder and who is this dear one?" "My wife, Willow. She's heavy with child and I'm wondering . . ." She cut him off. "Of course she's heavy with child, you think I'm blind," she admonished. Then she turned to Willow, who in complete bewilderment had been observing the on going dialogue. Then Pearl came to Willow and said, "you poor dear you must be plumb tired out and worn out. Come in here and lie down while I fix some vittles for all us."

Doc and Josh talked well into the night; a quart jar of moonshine melted away as their conversation proceeded. Josh revealed his intentions to leave Willow with them that he could meet his date with Sam Dale, where he had a job as an Indian scout and point rider for a wagon train. The train was being formed in Cades Cove, Gatlinburg, Tennessee, and he had only two weeks in which to travel there, and report in. "Josh, we barely have enough for two to survive, I can't work no more, black lung, and Pearl can barely handle the garden." "I understand," said Josh. "I'm not a rich man but I ain't broke. I will leave you a bounty of money for all of you to live on till I come back." Josh received a grateful and encouraging response. "We'll discuss this with the women folks in the morning," Doc said, and with that they stumbled into the house and turned in.

Josh and Willow had a tearful good-bye. "I'll be back to see you and our child soon as I can." He rode away, heading east to Bluefield and on towards Gatlinburg, several days ride away.

WAGON TRAIN

Chapter Three

THE WAGON TRAIN

In contrast to the frightening clientele dominating the roads and taverns which Josh had left behind, the vast entourage referred to as wagon train, were of a different breed. It consisted of "families" of settlers with a purpose and a destination. The horsepower was different. Wagon train mules were sleek, spirited, fast and sturdy as opposed to the heavy dray horses weighing a ton or more. Freight wagons differed in structure from that of the over land "prairie-schooners," found in wagon trains. These sleek vehicles were constructed for endurance and floating ability as well as some degree of comfort for the traveling family. By balancing the load, these schooners named "Conestoga's" (by the maker) could slither into a running river behind disciplined teams, and cross most any stream, emerging on the opposite bank, family in place, and dry. To endure the storms and the environment of the west, it was a must that the settlers secure a "Conestoga prairie-schooner." The tarpoleums were stretched over special bent bows and tied securely to the sides. In vain could the blistering wind and sand storms take the canvas top from its mooring. In vain could the hail beat down and rip away the family protection. Vulnerable, of course, to the Indian arrows tipped with fire, which could achieve penetration. The inside, under cover Conestoga resembled a fortress. Gun mounts, ammunition provisions, were built-in permitting immediate assistance from any and all members of the family on hand. The red warriors learned that close-in fighting was not always the best tactic.

The formation of wagon trains took much planning and preparation, as well as negotiating with settlers for safe passage to their destinations. It was a mammoth enterprise. American contractors were largely instigators of the wagon train movement. These entrepreneurs sought large grants of land in payment for bringing settlers into the newly formed states or territories. They were professionals; they were to a large extent men who had been tested in the fires of the region and risky adventure of penetrating the western frontier. Many had themselves blazed a trail westward. They were guided by the stars. Realizing the danger, securing a qualified scout and Indian fighter was a necessity. The wagon master was a celebrant and highly sought after. The members of the group underwent surveillance as to their ability to cope with the environ before them. Certain characteristic traits were helpful, if not required. A spirit of adventurous enterprise, a willingness to go through hardship or danger to accomplish an objective, was a distinct quality. People who think nothing of making a long journey, of encountering fatigue, and of enduring many species of hardship. Characteristically, men who could endure almost anything, who have lived almost without restraint, free as the mountain men, and who perceived being Americans was to act out their principles during their whole life; people who have an apparent roughness, which some may deem rudeness of manners.

These traits characterized especially the agriculture prospectors of the country and in some degree, the new towns and villages. These are the people of the west, who made up the occupants of thousands of prairie schooners seeking a place to build their cabins. They were not ignorant or barbaric as some would suppose, but the results of circumstances of people thrown together in a strange and new country. When people know but little about each other, there is perfect equality in the neighborhood, each being lord of the soil which is being cultivated. For years all they could expect was a log cabin. These circumstances lay the foundation for that equality of intercourse, simplicity of manners, want and deference, want of reserve, readiness to make acquaintances, and freedom of speech. This is the quality colonist looked for. This was the character of most wagon train contingents. This typified the strength behind the wagon train master, formulating a bastion of courage, an undaunted breed of pioneers.

General Sam Dale was uncompromising. The reckless and the faint hearted were eliminated at the origin of formulation. Dale also fully realized the challenge before him was to manage the security of the participants making up the train. This especially called for confrontation with seasoned Indians, employing the Indian way, by use of the long knife. Accordingly, General Dale kept Josh in mind as a key man in the safety of the entire wagon train. He needed a point rider he could depend on. The scrappy, happy mountain man filled this position.

General Dale summoned Josh to his wagon for an important conference. He had taken a great liking to Josh and had assigned him to the key security job of point rider. This entailed riding well ahead of the train, sometimes miles ahead, scouting the area for hostile natives. Being alone, and in constant peril, was nothing new to this seasoned mountain man. Josh relished his job. He took much pleasure in riding and communicating with his great horse. Roan seemed to perceive the responsibility assigned Josh and was alert for surprise attacks. The two together posed to challenge any impending dangers.

General Dale held a briefing with Josh. "When we reach

Mississippi we will be in hostile country." The Choctaws and the Creeks occupy an area 300 miles long, stretching along side of the big river, the Mississippi! A Creek savage by the name of Savannah Jack dominates the area. There was never known to be a meaner, more treacherous killer and scoundrel ever to infest any country. Savannah Jack's raiders lay in wait for wagon trains along the trails to Mississippi and Alabama. You can't avoid him, the General said. He will do the attacking. Every person in the train is responsible to remain alert and prepared. Your job, Josh, is to warn us in advance and give us a chance to survive. This was the most serious challenge ever undertaken by Josh. He accepted it and met it headlong with vigor and anticipation.

Josh was one of those unsung heroes sprung from the wilderness brand of living and plumped down in the midst of civilization. He was now a part of the great movement west to uncharted land, infested by hostile Indians, enraged over the invasion of their land. Josh was confident he could hold his own in meeting the challenge before him. Nevertheless, he was only human. He looked back on his life as he had lived it, and was hit with a shock. All he had accomplished was filling his days with a pile of tomorrow's dreams and an abundance of empty yesterdays. The needs of his wilderness life had been satisfied by wood and water, and a horse. The quality of life for a wagon train guide and Indian scout was couched entirely in the degree of alertness employed every minute of the day. From the pinnacle of a rocky ledge he could see the long row of white tops, creeping in single file, animated havens bearing families with dreams. They were going places. They had destinations, and they depended upon him to get them there safely. But he could not remain with them, put down roots, raise a family, sleep in a bed, eat freshly cooked food, work in a place of his own, a place to sleep peacefully and safely without relying on the proverbial gun ever in reach. Even at this very moment he sensed he was being watched. Nearby, could be cruel savages lying in wait, ready to vent their rage at being invaded by the "white-eyes." Josh's horse sensed the presence of danger and flared his nostrils and flicked his ears. Josh could feel his horse flexing his powerful muscles in preparation for a dash to safety. He figured it was time to "get out of here," and he touched the reins with a panic signal and the horse unloosed a burst of speed like a frightened coyote and not too soon. The jagged boulders strewn on the hillside like sentinels exploded with yelling and yapping red warriors. Astride their fleet footed mustangs, they swarmed down the hill and into the valley in hot pursuit. Josh's great roan loved the challenge. He paced himself far enough ahead to keep Josh at a safe distance. He seemed to know exactly what he was doing. Josh let him have his head, and cut him loose, void of directions. The two had been in this situation in numerous instances. Soon the pursuing red-man faded into the descending dusk and melted into their environ. Josh had accomplished his objective for the day; to ferret out the dangerous warriors and return to the train with news of the encounter, again emphasizing the ever present need for alertness to raids led by Savannah Jack. Josh smiled to himself. Just another day of dreams of tomorrow, to be filled with another empty yesterday.

Their train circled for the night and a state of preparedness implemented. General Dale, on his great white gelding, rode slowly around the groupings for assurance a state of readiness was in place.

During the first week of movement along the river, evidence of raids by the Choctaws and the Creeks were discovered. When the train reached the entrance of the Natchez Trace (near Tupelo), a wagon and family apparently traveling alone, lay smoldering, victims of an Indian raid. Two adult bodies found and evidence of children possibly taken as captives. General Dale was outraged. He formed a patrol of 30 men, with Josh in charge. They chased a band of Creeks off and on, but could never bring them to battle. The Indians, being constantly pursued and pressed, apparently crossed the Mississippi River and were never heard of again.

The occupants of the wagon train began to break up all along the delta and occupy the rich black lands as farmers. The Creeks decided to honor their treaty of 1814, giving up lands, and new settlers flooded into Mississippi territory. The population at that time was about 74,000. Large cotton plantations were created and slavery predominated.

ASIDE:

The lands produced abundantly and the prices were high. Planters plowed back their profits into buying more land and more slaves. Many became wealthy, and great mansions began to be built. By comparison, a New England farmer earned by hard labor perhaps $700.00 a year. A Natchez planter with the same acreage made 10 times more. His profits in good years were 30% on his investment; on 500 acres of cultivated land with the work of fifty slaves, a typical planter grew two hundred acres of cotton producing one hundred bales of four hundred pounds each, sold at twenty cents a pound, for a total of eight thousand dollars. His investment included land, slaves, and equipment totaled perhaps thirty-five thousand dollars.

But all was not paradise in Mississippi. The State earned the grim reputation as a most unhealthy place. Physicians were scarce and inclined to leave practice as soon as they could stake themselves to a cotton plantation. The settlers suffered from mosquito born disease of malaria and yellow fever. In bad years the death rate approached 10% of the population.

The State of Mississippi continued to be plagued with the Indian situation. They were a stubborn lot and untrustworthy and kept the settlers upset and on guard. Finally in October, 1820, near Canton at Doaks Stand, several hundred Choctaw Indians gathered, to be plied for three weeks with twenty thousand dollars worth of beef, corn and liquor. They were the quest of the U.S. Government. The Government leaders, who planned the event, were General Andrew Jackson and General Thomas Hinds, old Indian fighters from Creek wars, and heroes of the battle of New Orleans. The purpose of the gathering was to bribe the Indians to give up their lands in Mississippi and move west to a reservation. The chief, though objecting, but under threat, signed the agreement. Jackson promised 13 million acres in Arkansas and a territory in Oklahoma for 5 million more acres. This agreement merely cracked the door, as the Choctaws and Chickasaws did not leave. By late 1820, the pressure became too heavy to withstand. Jackson became President in 1829, and in 1830 the Mississippi lawmakers approved legislation removing the autonomous rights of the Indians who had remained in Mississippi. This coercion succeeded, and at a meeting with U.S. Government representatives at Dancing Rabbit Creek in eastern Mississippi, the Choctaws ceded the remainder of their lands, and agreed to a tribal exodus to new lands in Indian Territory. Two years later in 1832, the Chickasaws capitulated, and in the treaty of Pontotoc Creek, agreed to similar terms.

This tripled lands available for settlement and spurred a land rush to the area. In 10 years, 1830-1840, the population of Mississippi increased one hundred seventy-five percent, slave population by one hundred ninety-seven percent, and by 1840 blacks' out-numbered whites. Thirty new counties were created; and seven million acres were sold, much bought by speculators. The Federal Government set a price at one dollar twenty-five cents an acre minimum blocks of eighty acres. In 1835 alone, the public land office in Mississippi disposed of 3 million acres, most sold on credit, via paper bank notes, secured by land. Prices skyrocketed, but in 1837 Jackson decreed all sales must be cash and land paid for. The land bubble burst, prices plummeted, wildcat banks and speculators went broke in droves. Foreclosure notices, "settlers moved to Texas," leaving their debts behind, to start over again farther west.

Over a year had passed since Josh left Willow in her pregnant condition. He felt ashamed, and prayed softly to himself daily that all was well with her and child and the Purdy family. Obstacles beyond their control had caused the long delayed completion of the Alabama-Mississippi mission. Due to Constant Indian raids; sometimes they would be holed up in battle formation for days. Provisions dissipated, and replacement supplies scarce on this sparsely populated area. Josh was stuck. He could not abandon his assignment and race back to Willow at the time of his child's birth. Then one day Josh approached

Sam Dale "Sam I've got to go, you understand." "I certainly do, our job is close enough to being completed, get going." Then he remarked, "my friend, old hickory, has sent word he's thinking of impressing me into the immigration service on this Indian movement, but I plan to decline," and they departed.

Josh traveled north to St. Louis where he caught a keelboat part way to Pocahontas. The journey had consumed two full weeks. Mrs. Purdy set alone in a dim room rocking a child. She handed it sadly to Josh. He was startled. A blue blemish covered the child's left eye. It was a boy. Seeing his startled look, she explained.

Two days before its birth, Willow had fallen from the high porch, a plank had given way tripping her and causing the fall. She never recovered from her broken neck, but with the help of a local midwife she birthed the child. The birthmark resulted from her fall. Maybe, maybe not, but there it was permanently marking the kid for life. The other news, Doc Purdy had died two months ago and the black lung had gotten him, too. The boy was named Will at the request of Willow. He was now 7 months old.

Josh emptied his pocket book to Pearl. "I will send more when I get it. I'm thankful he has a home and you." He left never to see his son again. Pearl died 12 years after last seeing Josh. He had made no return trips. Will was orphaned at 12 years of age.

The year was 1832. Gains, Dale and Josh had observed the treaty with the Indians at Dancing Rabbit Creek. They rode away from the proceedings with heavy hearts, feeling deeply for the old chiefs as they in their own eloquence droned out their sorrow in ceding the last bit of their Mississippi land. Sam said, "there should have been a better way out for the Choctaws and the Chickasaws." Unfortunately, in the minds of the white man and that of the Federal Government the Indians were bloodthirsty outlaws, humans with no conscience, and must be eradicated or banished and contained elsewhere in some out-of-the-way lands.

Soon after the treaty of Dancing Rabbit Creek, the secretary of war appointed General Dale and Colonel George Gaines to supervise the removal of the Choctaws to their new home across the Mississippi river, in what is now Oklahoma and Arkansas. Dale could not resist President Jackson's appointment. Dale prevailed upon Josh to join him in this undertaking—an immigration project. Josh devoted the next two years to this most unpleasant task. The Indians did not want to go, leaving their buried ancestors behind. They would abandon the tribes as they moved grudgingly through the wilderness, and return to Mississippi only to be rounded up and brought along in the next movement. On one of these trips General Dale's horse stepped into a hole and fell on him, inflicting severe internal injuries. Being 60 years old and worn down by his rugged frontier life, he was forced to give up the immigration service. Josh had escorted Big Sam and his party back to Lauderdale County, Mississippi. Soon after the accident and his recovery, Dale left for Washington City to pay a visit to his old friend and fellow warrior, President Andrew "Ole Hickory" Jackson. Josh never saw Sam again.

Josh returned to his former business of escorting settlers to the new territory, but as years went by he became more discontented with his lot in life. He was now nearing the age of 35 and was beginning to wonder if he would end up like Sam Dale, 60 and single. Sam had no family, had never married, had no community roots, no church, no nothing. These thoughts wore heavily on Josh until one day he loaded his meager belongings on a sturdy packhorse, mounted his big roan stallion and headed for Texas.

When Josh had resumed his old profession of guiding settlers to their destination he got caught up in the vast movement of settlers going to Texas. The greatest attraction being the availability of large acreage of good lands, a veritable bonanza of soil. The soil in the eastern territory was highly adaptable to the system of agriculture, which settlers had used all the way from Pennsylvania to Mississippi, and now spilling over into Texas. Most were backwoodsmen coming westward with slaves and herds, seeking land in vast quantities. The trend was continuous. In the long range of Texas border history there was actually little or no break in the expansion of the American frontier settlement, from Susquehanna to the Rio Grand.

Josh was fascinated by the territory of Texas, and when he crossed the Mississippi river into Louisiana and Texas, he visioned he was in a new country. Though the invasion of Texas, while under Spanish rule, dated back to 1790-1800, it was the first years of the Nineteenth Century when the settler invasion moved in full force. The migration rose and fell with the political and religious climate invoked by the Spanish government. Effective colonization began with the efforts of Stephen F. Austin in 1821. He promised to bring 50 families to colonize a portion of Texas, to embrace the catholic religion and swear allegiance to the laws of Mexico. He proposed a system of land grants. Men were to be given 640 acres, married men an additional 320 plus 160 acres for each child, and 80 for each slave. Thus a married man with four children and two slaves would be entitled to 1,800 acres.

The huge land bounty promised by Austin was a great temptation to the frontiersman. 50 families from Nacogdoches made the move to the new Texas Eden. Elsewhere in the old west families were anxious to make the move.

ASIDE:

Opening of Texas to settlement in 1826 was the most timely incident in frontier history. The depression (panic) of 1819 had taken a heavy economic toll of settlers who had pushed to the fringe of civilization. It was not until 1823 that Austin received final approval from the government to colonize. A revision had been made in the land grants (less generous): heads of families were to receive 170 acres, cattle grazing 4428 acres, no slaves allowed, and families had six years to improve their land. The impresario (promoter) received generous grants of land and a fee of $0.125 per acre when he had settled the project of colonization. There too, Texas Government was granting huge blocks of *land in western Texas to be settled illegally and un-speculative. Settlers arrived and cleared land already occupied and being farmed by New Mexico residents. This land had been wrested from Mexico under the Mexico-US war of 1848-49. Much unrest existed between the inhabitants, and the new settlers. This, together with the marauding Comanches made life in western Texas untenable. Many stayed long enough to construct home sites but then abandoned.*

In 1845, Texas had won its independence from Mexico, and had been admitted to the Union as its 28th state. But the treasury was so bare that it could not provide outlying ranches and settlements with protection against Indian attacks. Governor Sam Houston established the "minute men" of Texas, a volunteer organization of thousands. Armed settlers gathered in small units stationed about 100 miles from each other, in a line southwest from Preston on the Red River to the Mexican border on the Rio Grande. This line followed the route of the southern overland mail, which had the protection of a chain of forts that the Federal Government built across Texas from Colbert's Ferry on the Red River to Cedar Lake, Fort Lobo on the border of New Mexico. These forts were primarily for the safe passage of gold seekers streaming to California.

The "protection" attracted hundreds of immigrants who were arriving by covered wagon to make Texas their new home. Up to 200 wagons a day were reported moving down the "Texas Road." The compelling factor that kept them coming was knowledge that a farmer could find free land in Texas. There were none who arrived without some knowledge of danger in living in north central Texas. Most all had heard the story of the Indian attack on Parkers Fort, a lonely stockade far out on the Navasota River. This happened in 1836 when the entire Parker family was massacred with the exception of a child, Cynthia, and her younger brother, John. They were taken captive and raised as Indians, and Cynthia grew up to become the wife of Peta Nocona, Comanche Chief. Born to them was a son, Quanah, in 1854, at the Comanche's strong hold at Cedar Lake. He later became the last surviving Chief of the murdering Comanches.

The red warriors of Texas continued to strike with intense savagery, sparing no one regardless of age or sex, mutilating the dead and *destroying and burning what they did not want or could not carry off, instilling terror in the hearts of the settlers. The responsibility of colonization fell on the shoulders of Stephen F. Austin. No other frontier leader possessed his common sense and tact. He informed himself on the problems of the Mexican Government and knew precisely the pattern of behavior, which the American Colonist would have to follow to secure official sufferance. The Mexican Government owned Texas Territory. Austin scouted the lands, which he wished to claim. These were located between the Guadalupe and the Colorado Rivers and six leagues above the Texas-Nacogdoches road and down the Brazos-San Jacinto watershed to the Gulf. The land grants he secured for the settlers were generous. Austin received his fee for bringing the settlers of $0.125 per acre, having succeeded in developing a wagon train arriving with three hundred families to settle on Texas land.*

The willingness to follow Austin to Texas was an example of the American psychosis to move away to lands free from present troubles. Three hundred families following Austin down the "Texas highway" was an awesome movement. Population growth was amazing. By the year 1828 there were 2028 settlers, by 1830 4,248 and 5,665 in 1831. These and other settlements mushroomed to 30,000 five years later.

The "Highway to Texas" was jammed with problems. The native Indians were enraged at the land giveaway policy being practiced by the government of Mexico and promiscuously vented their feelings by marauding, pillaging, scalping and taking captives, young boys, and especially young girls. The children were traded to Mexican bandit gangs who held them for ransom. Teamsters were murdered and teams stolen; herds were seized and run off. A man of Josh's status, experienced teamster, wagon master, scout and Indian fighter was much in demand. Josh was sickened at the thought of being caught up in this amalgamate of a "Texas Eden." He had his sights set on something more to his character and liking, the cattle industry.

According to Josh, a characteristic summary of the Texas condition was a remark he overheard; "Texas was hard on women and oxen." No doubt it was. Hundreds of letters written back depicted a fear status, in Mississippi, Alabama, Tennessee, Kentucky, letters told both of the extreme hardships and the wonderful opportunities in the new land. "Gone to Texas" became a meaningful legend in the older states. Men came to escape debts or impending arrest for crimes. Their wives and children in numerous instances succumbed to exhaustion and their own frustrations.

To the new Eden, sheriffs ran away and left their badges and altercations behind, farmers abandoned fields, ministers deserted their pulpits, and enterprises of every sort rushed west to the rising new state. Within 3 years from the time Josh arrived, the population of Texas grew from 20,000 to 200,000, increasing at the rate of 1000 per week. When Texas entered the union in 1845, they did so largely on their own terms and it was not without an enormous amount of pride that they proclaimed this achievement. Texas frontiersmen were sentimentalists. When the flag was struck on Feb 16, 1846 there was a show of genuine emotion.

The annexation of Texas to the union touched off a chain reaction of events, which ran a full course between 1845 and 1861. It was during this era that Josh outfitted himself to become one of the largest cattle barons in west Texas.

CATTLE DRIVE TO DODGE CITY

Chapter Four

THE CATTLE DROVERS

Josh's last train disbanded in the Bexar County area, where Stephen F. Austin's massive land holdings were. Having observed thousands of herd of wild cattle, and having knowledge of the abundance of free land in the state of Texas. Josh figured Texas was his final destination. In Texas with luck, he would start up his ranch and become a gentleman Cattle Baron. To reach this point it would be necessary for him to become heavily engaged in the cattle business, such as acquiring large herds of cattle for his range, wherever that would be. Trailing herds of 2000 to 5000 head at a time would soon amount to many bucks. The pay ran from $3 to $5 per head. Trailing a heard of 5000 over a distance of 1200 miles required a crew of 20 or more Cowboys who were paid a salary of $1 and keep a day. The net was favorable. Josh was determined to get into the Drover business. He headed for San Antonio to commence his venture.

Josh pulled up at the hitching rail of the Wild Pitch saloon in San Antonio. He loosely tied his big horse, now a Zebra Dunn stallion, and looked around curiously at his surroundings. Mostly Mexican, and a number of Anglo-Americans, sometimes calling themselves Texicans, occupied the town, which was struggling with a new government. The country was rife with lawlessness and inhabited by hostile Indians and Mexicans. In November, 1835 Houston officially organized a statewide police force known as the Ranging Men, later as the Texas Rangers. This was done largely to protect the settlers from marauding Comanches and thieving Mexicans. The attraction to Josh, however, was the three million longhorn wild cattle roaming the territory just waiting for the market. He felt his future was a ranch, a herd of his own, or being a drover contractor trailing herds to the nearest rail siding for shipment north, the nearest being Dodge City and Abilene Kansas. He sat out to make the right contact to explore this profession.

In San Antonio he immediately went in search of drovers. He became aware of his attire as not conforming to that of a typical cowman. He felt very comfortable by conforming to the dress of the so-called "aristocrats of the saddle," the cowboy. The majority wore denim jeans of the backcountry store trade, and a wide brim Mexican sombrero, or a wide brim black wool hat. They wore high-heeled sharp-toed boots, which were designed for safety. The chaps were worn to prevent brush from tearing trousers and scratching legs. Both the wool vest and bandanna had high utilitarian value. The vest was to carry tobacco, watch, paper and matches, and any other miscellaneous supplies. The bandana was both a neck shade and a dust filter. Topping all this was a cartridge belt and holster, which hung from the hips. The revolver was a necessary tool of the cattle trade. It served to stop the charge of a maddened steer, kill a rattlesnake, or a noisemaker to turn back a frightened stampeding herd. Sometimes a revolver was necessary for self-defense against Indians and rustlers. Some cowboys were careless with their side arm, forgetting their lethal nature and shooting off in public places, and at people for fun. This caused trouble, however, this was an exception as most Cowboys seldom, if ever, carried a gun into town, or in public.

Josh outfitted himself well, discarding his buckskin frontier garb, he outfitted himself with high-heel boots, and tall crowned hat, and his 6'3" frame cut a striking figure. He mixed well with the milling cowhands, looking for a chance to sign-on with drovers, in search of adventure. Trailing cattle to Dodge City and to Abilene, Kansas with a chance to engage marauding Indians and rustlers intrigued the young and restless. Josh was concerned over his lack of experience on the trail, and wandered about how drovers would view these anxious cowboys, with no drover experience. He soon found out however, that true drovers were not anxious to sign-on just anyone, regardless of experience. Drovers did not fear the man's ability to ride long and hard, or to fight when fighting was necessary, rather their concern was the cowboys trustworthiness. Men in the trail driving business often found themselves in a life-threatening predicament. If one man lost his nerve and turned yellow in face of danger it could imperil the life of others.

ASIDE:

In a chance encounter, while delivering settlers to north Texas, Josh's patrol, engaged a group of Comanches attacking a herd being trailed to Abilene. It was Josh's wagon train occupants who came to the rescue of the drovers. They scattered the renegade marauders, and continued to move safely to their destination, which was Denton, Texas. After the skirmish, the trail boss rode into the wagon train rendezvous and met Josh. Joe Thorpe, the trail boss, also being of 6'3" stature admired Josh and invited the train to trail behind his herd until they reached Denton. The camaraderie that developed between these two stalwarts was rewarding. Josh learned much about the character of the trail drovers and the business itself. One day, he promised himself, he would be a trail boss like Joe.

On a hot afternoon, Joe Thorpe set his dapple gray under a spreading Oak. He surveyed the valley below, squinting from under a boss raw edge Stetson. His eyes were dark and brooding. He sensed keenly, the awesome responsibility to trail 5000 head of cattle to Dodge City. The herd had been rounded up from four different spreads covering a 4 county area in south Texas. A normal trail herd consisted of 2500 head, at most. Now he was confronted with twice that. He could do it if he was lucky enough to find the manpower. He would split the herd and, trail in tandem. He would handle one, the lead herd; if he could come up with a second trail boss he would have it made. The situation was critical.

The ranchers had held back their cattle from a temporarily flooded market. Then the drought hung on longer than expected. Grass got shorter by the day and herds were deteriorating from pure emaciation. If they didn't get them on the way to a railhead they ran the risk of heavy losses. This condition was now having the effect of running the market up, and accelerating a sense of urgency, the sense of urgency expressed by ranchers.

Joe was eager to take on contracting to trail another herd north to the market. However, this had one drawback; it was too soon to re-enlist his regular drovers. They usually required at least two weeks off, just loafing, drinking, and spending their wages. Being on the trail two months, one way, took a lot out of a man. The ranchers had gathered their herds in advance of Joe's return; the drought was still on, grass was short, and it was urgent to get their herds on the way. Joe wanted the job as over 5000 head were involved; the price had gone to $5 a head, a lot of money. He rode into San Antonio with a gut feeling it would be difficult, if not impossible to get a crew of drovers right away.

At the longhorn saloon, downturn San Antonio a party was going on. There was laughter, drinking, music and dancing. When Joe arrived, almost simultaneously as he walked through the half-swinging doors, he was pinned against the wall. An altercation broke out between the frolicking young Cowhand and a fiddler who thought it was time to knock it off. When the fiddler stopped the music and started for home, some said let him go, others demanded he stay. A free for all broke out just inside the door. Josh was a part of the party. He had stepped aside to observe the young buckaroos working off their excess, pent-up energy. When Joe hit the wall under a pile of flailing arms he went down momentarily, then bounced up and bodily picked up a man and tossed him blindly. To his surprise a huge man, equally the size Joe caught the young cowboy in his arms and calmly walked toward him. He dropped him at Joe's feat and let out a yell. Both men clasped each other and Josh demanded silence. Josh yelled out, "men this is Joe Thorpe, the most famous drover in the country. The man we've been looking for." He turned to Joe, "We need a job and what are our chances?"

Joe could hardly believe his good fortune. Locating Josh and Josh having on hand a number of cowboys anxious for a job. The rowdy men gathered around, facing two giant men, leaning casually on the bar, drink in hand. What a pair they observed, and what a thrill it would be to ride with these knights of the range, Indian fighters, drovers, and leaders.

Then Joe spoke. "Men, I'm under contract to deliver 5000 head of cattle to Dodge City. The herds are being formed now. I need 20 men to do the job. It's a 1200-mile trip, takes two months to get there." "You've got em," someone called out. Then they shouted in unison "we're ready." "Are you experienced drovers?" Joe asked. Dead silence. "They're just a good bunch of cowboys, Joe. I know I've been with them several days. Good men," Josh stated. Then Joe explained his trail. "We will be going right smack through Comanche territory, and you can expect plenty of action to protect the herds. Reckon if you can ride and shoot you're qualified." A roar of delight.

"Okay men, drink up. It'll be your last time for a while. The sporting houses of Dodge are two months away. We'll be moving out in a couple of days." Joe and Josh tipped their glasses, shook hands, and smiled.

Josh was skeptical of his lack of experience as a trail boss. He was well aware of a drovers qualifications. They had to know their geography, cut out of a pattern of terrain; they had to know the lay of the land and be able to find water holes, safe stream crossings and grass. The men had to know how to manage herds, cut losses and endure up to 1200 miles on the trail. Joe had advised Josh they would be trailing in tandem, with Josh and his 2500 head trailing about 5 to 10 miles behind Joe's herd. This system would help Josh to acquire "on the job" training. He was confident he could handle it. Josh accepted the job, and agreed to select his own men out of the 20 or so applicants on hand. He would need 8 to 12 to handle the 2500 head herd, and to mount the men he would need a remuda of 80 to 125 horses. The remuda required an experienced wrangler to watch over and keep the animals abreast the chuck wagon, which was drawn by a pair of mules. The chuck wagon was driven by a cook who would move more rapidly than a grazing herd in order to establish camp and have food ready for the men. Sometimes, drovers would outfit their crew with night herders, called "hawks," so that the day riders could get uninterrupted sleep. This however, seldom materialized. Cowboys were often called upon to stand night watch of two or three hours each, and if the cattle were nervous or rustlers in the area, watching may last all night. A drover's life was not a glamorous or easy one.

Selecting men capable of enduring, or willing, to take on a drover's job was an exercise in risk management. Once you were underway, the Cowboy was compelled to stick it out. There was no turning back; else the entire crew would be endangered.

For a drive to reach the rail heads of Abilene and Dodge City, Kansas, with final destination markets of St. Louis and Chicago, involved a drive of several hundred miles, across dry country, through Indian territory, and over farm land where irate farmers were encountered, sometimes resulting in fierce battles and loss of lives.

Josh's young men, who obviously looked to him as their mentor, were all experienced cowboys, but they had never had any experience at trail driving. There was quite a difference in ranch labor and trailing cattle to the market. Both were strenuous work, hard, grimy, and without glamour. Herding wild cattle was always hazardous. A rampant bull, or a cow with a young calf, could show a lot of fight. Wild cattle milling about could gore and trample a man to death. Indians, rattlesnakes, wolves and coyotes also could make life precarious for the unarmed men. These men, all cowboys, had been toughened by the way of the range; riding range alone was a lonesome business. Sometimes cowboys would be gone from the ranch house and human association for extended periods. Range riders had to adapt themselves to course food of his own cooking, to sleeping on the ground, and to many other hardships. His daily work consisted of driving cattle back on home ranges, branding calves, running off strays, rounding up and counting grazing heads, and keeping a look out for Indians, and rustlers.

Trailing herds was somewhat of a different lifestyle. First, herds were initially assembled by the ranchers and their cowboys, branded and identified, and formed into a herd for the drovers. During the first day of the drive the cattle were a most fractious to stampede, playing havoc with the herd and herders. Almost any unusual thing could send their cattle on a rampage; electric storms, thunder, or the snort of a cowboy's horse in the night. Worst of all were the planned stampedes by the Indians and rustlers. Night herders sang continually, so that drowsing steers would not be startled by their presence.

Joe Thorpe signed on all 20 men, Josh's entire group of cronies, whom he had learned to appreciate with great respect. They assembled at a rendezvous point for commencement of the drive. Within two days the herds began to arrive.

After ten days on the trail, and all going well, Joe rode back a full half day, and intercepted Josh. He had a keen desire to put a challenge to Josh. To spark up the dull edge of the routine drive. Joe suggested Josh be on his own from here to Dodge and take a bet on arrival time. Optional trails of previous drovers were coming up. Josh was not one to pass up a game regardless of the stakes. The bet was on.

The bet was a mistake, and serious consequences occurred. Joe Thorpe became so imbued with the challenge to beat Josh to Dodge City his judgment became warped, violating his many years of trailing experience. He ran into trouble. Joe took a short cut, ignoring optional "proven" trails, a threatening peril to the herd. Joe's expedient trail kept the cattle from water so long they were both maddened and blinded. Most drovers preferred to add miles to their trip rather than cover long treacherous waterless stretches. Joe went against his "wisdom of the trail" and made up two days on Josh, but he lost over 300 head from his 2500.

It had been two weeks since he and Joe had made their bet. Shortly after that last meeting two of Josh's more seasoned riders conferred with Josh on an "open country" trail to the western frontier of Texas, by way of the south plains. They had served out an enlistment with the federal troops stationed in a small garrison called Fort Lobo. It was the heart of the Comanche Indian Territory. Their summer campground being Cedar Lake, a ceremonial burial ground. The garrison of troops was there to protect settlers. Fort Lobo was a small village containing the notorious lobo's den, a house of iniquity of the worst sort. There was lush grassland and ample water. Good place to bed down the herd for a few days and partake of a little R and R for the men.

Josh was impressed with this bit of information and confident he could direct his herd safely thru Cedar Lake and to Dodge City. However, being an experienced Indian fighter and scout, he perceived the Comanches a menace. "Lords of the plains," they dubbed themselves. Relishing a fight, he proceeded west to Cedar Lake and the Lobo's Den.

Cedar Lake and the infamous cowtown of Lobo was ideal for resting the herd and giving the riders a break. The Lobo's den was a notorious den of iniquity, a brothel second to none. There drovers celebrated, partaking freely of the town's generous supply of liquor, gambling, and women of the night.

Josh participated with his men. They had done a great job

of pushing the herd of 2500 to this halfway point and without loses. Being their leader and a legendary practical joker they trashed tender feet, stuffed strangers with weird stories, held kangaroo courts, and put on mock gun battles in which obnoxious braggarts were forced to show their feathers or run. Josh was a master in telling tall tales of the trail, and shocked the crowd at the lobo's den in a spectacular display of bravery and guts. He had an unexpected encounter with a notorious gunman, who was seeking favors from one of the ladies of the night, and was openly spurned. "You stink, you haven't had a bath in months," she yelled. She spun around practically in Josh's arms. "He's dangerous," she whispered and hastened away. Josh's rollicking sense of humor and love for practical joking couldn't resist accosting the stranger. He approached the gunman proffering drinks. He received a sullen look, and no thanks. Undaunted, Josh expressed admiration for the revolver strapped on his side. A pearl handle Russian made .44. He asked if he could see it and hold it. The gunman reluctantly lifted it from the holster, perplexed. Josh admired the gun, spun it on his fingers, mimicked the quick draw and put on a showy demonstration. The gunman stood in awe at the antics of this fun-loving "clown." Smiling a grateful thanks Josh returned the gun. Then to the stark amazement of the saloon patrons, Josh said, "why did the pretty lady jerk away from you? You look like a nice guy." "She said I stink and need to take a bath?" "Well you do stink, a bath would help clean the air around here." "You talk too much. If you don't shut-up, I'm calling you," blurted the gunman. He stepped out from the bar, Josh laughed loudly. "Now wait just a minute here," Josh protruded his left hand at the gunman's face. "Let's stop that "Call" stuff. I don't want to get killed, and I don't want to kill you." The gunman whipped out his revolver and pointed it at Josh's face. "Now look here, you about to make me mad," Josh said sternly. "You pull the trigger and I'll blow you in two." Josh slowly pulled his .44. "Put that gun away and go take a bath like the lady said. Just be sure you don't pull that trigger or you won't need a bath where you're going." His steel gray eyes bored in from slants on Josh's face. The people gasped. The gunman reluctantly holstered his gun and walked out of the saloon. The crowd sighed with relief. Josh smiled and with his left hand he dumped six cartridges on the bar.

Josh was proud of his hard riding fun-loving "aristocrats" of the saddle. Men, who according to the staid standards of the sober settlers, were sinful people, drunkards, speed maddened fiends, astride horses, seducing women; gunmen and a menace to peace and decency. Actually, the cowboy's mode of life was dramatically opposite that of the settler with his plodding institutions and reliance upon law and order.

Josh and his men "got'em up" and "moved'em out" onto Indian Territory, across the Oklahoma prairies and on to Kansas. Joe had preceded him by 5 full days, but when he learned that Josh's herd of 2500 had incurred no major losses, he held back on criticism of the late arrivals. After all he hadn't done so well in cutting his losses. They had a "double" and promised to meet again in San Antonio, some day.

The railhead cow town of Dodge City was the most famous of all; it consisted largely of cattle pens, rail sidings, saloons, hotels, dance halls, houses of prostitution, and gambling dens. It later became a frontier military outpost and buffalo hunter outfitting station. Dodge City became a magic name in range cattle history. Josh continued his engagement in trailing herds, extending over a ten-year period, 1835 to 1845. During this time he became quite fond of a madam owner of the Wild-Card saloon. On one of Josh's final drives, Hazel, told Josh of her plans to sell out and move to Abilene where she planned to join a former associate. Not until then had Josh yielded to his desire to spend the night with her. They never saw each other again.

During the ten years of trailing herds. Josh accumulated thousands of head of cattle. He took in cows for pay instead of cash. He pastured his growing herd on the free lush grassland in the cedar lake area.

Josh leased from the Sate of Texas, thousands and thousands of acres of lush grasslands. Here he developed his vast herds, cutting out hundreds from trail herds, which now were being moved by the thousands along the trail blazed by Josh Epps. He paid Dodge City prices, but some ranchers wondered about how the Comanches seemed to find a market for their acquisitions, taken at the expense of frequent stampedes occurring on the trail. It was pretty well known that Josh chose his hired hands from adventuresome characters and if tinged with lawlessness the better. Josh's men were referred to as his hired-gunmen. During the period from '45 to '55 Josh and his hand picked gunmen took small herds into the Colorado gold villages and found lucrative markets for meat. Prices were much higher than Dodge City and Josh enjoyed a profitable mark up on cattle acquired from drovers passing through. He pursued this financial venture off and on to the outbreak of the Civil War.

On this final trailing episode, Josh observed a herd of Buffalo, which he estimated to be two miles wide and ten miles long. They were in their annual migration from one breeding ground to another more fertile one across the Canadian and the Red River valley. Josh was fascinated, and promised himself he would check into the "hide hunting" business which seemed to be an attraction to the venturesome entrepreneur. Later, in Dodge City, he had a discussion with a buffalo hide hunter outfitter, and picked up the information needed to launch a new career. He returned to Lobo and called upon the madam of the brothel and village saloon, the Lobo's Den.

Vashti didn't look the part of a madam of a house of ill repute. Naive as Josh was, he could not see her as a "lady of the night." She ruled the girls, the men, and their activity. She was dressed in black leather, tight fitting pants and vest, over a yellow silk blouse. She was a golden blonde, blue-eyed beauty. On her hip was the ever-present pearl-handled .32 caliber pistol in a silver trimmed holster. To most folks the pistol was for show, however, this myth was dispelled one evening when and over zealous cowhand insisted on taking one of her girls to his camp. He called Vashti's bluff and that was the demise of that cowboy.

Josh admired Vashti. My kind of a woman, he thought. Wonder how she got here, he pondered. Soon he learned she had shown up with a slick gambler and hired gun that acquired the den for his boss by being faster on the draw than the owner. The "boss" in turn lost the den in a notorious poker game, and the hired gun found himself owner. Vashti, now his side kick and gun moll took over. Her partner didn't last long due to an encounter with a man named Pelham Ware, an under-cover agent for the cattleman's association. Seems the hired-gun den owner had been disclosed as ringleader of an organized band of rustlers, which had outraged the ranchers.

Josh refused to think Vashti was a "lady of the night." She was making plenty of money and didn't need that source of income. But her girls did, and they were a source of whisky income for the saloon. The place was obviously rife with the lawless. They came down from Lincoln County, New Mexico, on the lamb, or found themselves a hiding place from Texas Rangers. The Lobo's Den was a haven for cattle rustlers and scheming ranchers building their herds through illicit means. Hired guns were plentiful, and available for "special" assignments. Seldom had an evening gone by without a shoot-out or an altercation of some sort.

Josh soon gained the reputation of "Cattle Baron," the most likeable character around. People had a high respect for him, and admired his attitude and generosity. He could spot a man or woman down on their luck and he always had a kind word or some sort of accommodation and show of compassion. Rustlers feared him as having some strange power to see right through them.

Vashti, loving attention, took a great liking to Josh. When his large frame was outlined in the doorway to the den, she would coyly announce "well look who's here," meet him, and escort him to her personal tables. Josh was infatuated but he had gumption enough to realize this was the nature of her business. Every drifter who came along wanted to buy Vashti a drink. They could not resist that leather-clad figure with the Caribbean blue eyes, accentuated with the yellow scarf. She always refused the drink; only with Josh would she sip at a brandy.

The limited courtship between Josh and Vashti was going smoothly. They were a handsome couple; his seniority and mature stature, stately as it was, complimented her vivacious beauty. She sat close to him, liking to a fresh prairie flower waiting to be consumed by an indiscriminant bovine. Many expected them to get hitched.

Disaster struck Josh, a catastrophic event that changed their lives forever and the whole countryside mourned. Vashti had set the date for the nuptials and was determined to have a wedding second to none ever performed on the Texas frontier. She accompanied Josh to his ranch headquarters, modest at the time. During the afternoon Vashti was involved deeply in preparation, discussing with Josh's foremen, who was designated the duty of putting on "a big one." Josh was napping in the shade of the back porch when three uniformed men of the federal forces rode up. The War Between the States was heating up and the union army was out to establish a source of meat. The sergeant in charge asked for Josh and discussed potential supplies of beef. Josh and the sergeant rode away to inspect his herds and the two enlisted men opted to rest their horses and stretched out in shadows of the late afternoon. One produced a bottle. By dusk the bottle was empty and Josh and the sergeant had not returned. Vashti and the Forman completed their discussion of wedding plans, and she returned to the small ranch house and entered the back door. The two enlisted men, fired up over the sight of this walking beauty, stirred from their prone position on the porch and slipped thru the door, dragging Vashti to her knees and then onto the bed, ripped off her jacket and tearing at her skirt. One man was on her, the other pinning her to the bed. Josh walked in on the struggle. The sergeant pulled his service revolver and shot the man, in the act of rape, killing him instantly. The other man jumped up to run but was blocked by Josh who was unarmed. Before the sergeant could turn on him for a lethal shot, the soldier drove his stiletto deep into the groin of Josh severing his lower spinal cord. Josh was paralyzed for life. The foreman appeared on the scene, and he and Vashti tended Josh who stared blankly into the night. The sergeant dragged the two dead soldiers away. There was no medical doctor in Lobo, but the federal garrison, was staffed with a surgeon and a medic where Josh remained in his care for a weeks but the feeling had gone out of his lower body. Obviously, he was doomed for the wheel chair. What about Vashti and their wedding? Wouldn't be fair, she has a lot of living to do, thought Josh.

The wedding was postponed indefinitely, however Vashti moved in. She took tender loving care of Josh and being the vixen she was, her motives were sensual and conniving. "I will be living with you as your caregiver, if not your lover," Vashti said. "I want your name. I want to be known as Vashti Epps." "I will see my friends, Joe Merritt, the Judge, and he will take care of that," Josh replied, and he did.

Month after month, Josh applied every means of physical therapy but his lower body did not respond. The fall roundup came and went. He helped design and fashion a means to access a buckboard in which he rode the range alone, driving two sleek mustangs. His life was drifting away to a stone lonesome existence. He appreciated Vashti, and loved her, but of late she seemed to be drifting away. Her attitude had turned with a ting of mockery, away from that of compassion. She would sometimes dress in glittery lace and flowering gown and parade before him, teasing? I don't know, thought Josh. Maybe trying to arouse some sexual feelings, but it never happened, and Josh would stare sadly out the window.

The cunning Vashti had Josh wrapped up, as well as the entire kingdom of the lazy "V," foreman and all.

Josh proceeded to build a mansion at the west end of Cedar Lake, which looked down the full length of the off-white alkalie space, no water, just a spectacular sea of alkaline; the serenity punctured only by the howl of the lobo wolves and the yapping of the coyotes.

Vashti became a nuisance around the ranch, flaunting her body, short skirted, and showing off her booted shapely legs. Men were tempted to take her to the hayloft, and on one occasion a newly hired hand was shot to death by the foreman who failed to tell the kid who she was. Men soon became disenchanted by her antics and drifted away. She seemed to always have a ready replacement, unsavory as they were, and wearing the proverbial low-slung, tied down .44.

Vashti was permanently and solidly enthroned as the Baroness of the Lazy "V", the grassland empire built by the brave and fearless mountain man, guide, and drover. He had never suspicioned Vashti having a connection with the highly organized rustler element plaguing the ranchers; he now wondered about the new gun moll who took over the madam's position at the Lobo's Den, named Utoka Jett. And what he didn't know was that the vagabond guitar player, Pelham Ware was an undercover agent for the cattleman's association.

In the annals of Texas range land there never was known a more cunning and deceitful, hateful, person than Vashti Epps. As reigning queen of Texas largest cattle kingdom, cattleman despised her with a suspicion. Her continued contact with the hired gun element hanging out at her ranch and at the Lobo's Den, met with much disfavor and eyebrow lifting. Josh's herds seem to be growing while others were dwindling.

TEXAS RANGER

Chapter Five

THE RANGING MEN

Will Purdy was orphaned at an early age. The twelve year old was left alone in a small cabin to scrounge for himself. For four years he was isolated from companionship or parenthood, and by necessity, lived by the ways of the forest. He was basically illiterate, having no formal schooling available. He could neither read nor write. He grew up with uncouth teamsters, trappers, and adventures, existing on their handouts and cast off clothing. He was literally a forest urchin. Deserted by his mountain man father as an infant, he struggled for existence.

Will was a tall, lean, lanky kid. His hard features were swarthy; steel gray eyes depicted a fearless attitude. His appearance belied his youthful 16 years. Staying alive was an achievement; to grow into adulthood a matter of acute accomplishment. Wild animals and Indians were lumped together and considered his competition. He studied them both, their stealthy movement, their hunting prowess and natural skills of survival, and the Indians ability to use the long knife, and tomahawk, of which he himself was quite skillful. He observed their ways and methods of capturing game and wild animals, sometimes, with their bare hands. Will's ambition was to achieve the skill of the red man, which, even at an early age, he succeeded to a great extent.

Will was shy to public exposure, partly because of the embarrassment of the ugly birthmark covering his left eye. He took up the habit of wearing a soft, black bear skin patch fastened about his head with two thongs. To develop stability and equilibrium he found it necessary to wear the patch continuously; he never became handicapped in anyway by this affliction.

Will longed for adventure, but travel was impeded by not having a horse, and his chance to come by one was slim to none, yet, he could not overlook the abundant wild horses running loose in the forest. His intense desire for a horse compelled him to take up a vigil near a strategic watering hole, frequented daily by the leader of the pack, a sleek Zebra dun stallion; the most beautiful animal will had ever seen. He dreamed daily of being astride the dun, riding swiftly through the weeded terrain and the open fields of grass. Silently and deathly still, Will practiced the Indian's tactics. Some days the stallion came so close he could have touched him. Will waited. Soon the stallion sniffing at Will, motionless he lay and let the stallion satisfy his curiosity. Day after day, the magnificent animal with the wicked eyes came to visit Will, as if waiting for him to come alive. Will said to himself. . . This is my horse. We have a future together. With this in mind he fashioned a means to capture the horse. At their next encounter, Will appeared hours ahead of the normal time, anchored a lariat rope to a nearby tree, fashioned a loop to lay across his body, and then stretched out on the rock to await the arrival of the stallion. He came as usual, sniffed at Will's prone body and Will deftly and quickly slipped the noose over the horse's head. This was the first time the horse had seen any sign of life in this human being, and with a loud snort he sprang away. The noose tightened, and the great stallion was anchored to the tree.

Will did not move. He let the horse wear himself down, and left him there for the night. The next day he came and sat still and silently on the rock the entire day. He left again, leaving the horse anchored for the night. Will continued this practice for two more days. On the third day of captivity, he approached the docile and famished horse, patted him gently, and whispered in his ears. Will continued to do so a number of times during the day, before releasing the rope from the tree. With rope in hand he started walking down a trail leading to a water hole. The horse followed; somehow Will felt he would. They reached the bank, the horse eagerly plunged his nose deep to take on much needed water. Will leaped to his back and the horse lunged forward into shoulder deep water, and he deftly forced the stallion to tread water and wade for several hours with Will clinging tightly astride. Hours later the two emerged from the water and moved slowly down the trail toward Will's camp, both exhausted.

Will named the horse "Jones," but for no particular reason, it just sounded good. He spent week after week breaking Jones, to the saddle, and to carrying a pack while negotiating narrow trails around cliffs, and forging streams. When Will felt Jones was ready to travel he saddled up, packed, and hit the trail for parts unknown.

Stories of the western frontier had intrigued the vision of the young outdoorsman. The Indian fighting, wagon trains, and cattle drives generated a sense of adventure. Now with a well-broken wild horse, together with his expert ability with the rifle and side arm, the long knife and tomahawk, Will felt competent and brave. He struck out for Texas. He had listened to the tall tales of Texas from Wagoneer's; about free land, wild cattle, and cowboys. Jones traveled well and obediently. They cut days off the distance and when Will arrived in Fort Worth he found other young men hanging out at the stock yards; young hopefuls looking for a job, a connection with ranchers. They were to soon find out their chosen professions was not as glamorous as anticipated.

ASIDE:

The State of Texas was half settled and half frontier, and swarming with four million longhorn waiting for the market. Texas was larger than the original thirteen states, and the great plains alone covered one-third million square miles.

Will Purdy did not tarry long in Fort Worth. He rode westward to Weatherford where he later settled on a large spread and became engaged in routine ranch work, his objective to gain experience. He viewed the vastness of the Texas cattle country a challenge and he was to contain a part of it. There were abundant herds of longhorns available for those who could withstand the rugged, lonely, life on the frontier. Will was determined to acquire a herd of his own, intersect a drover and send his herd north to a hungry market. Dreaming? Very definitely, it doesn't work out that way!

Will worked the roundups and spent months in the extensive unpopulated area. He was amazed at the herds of wild cattle gathered from the mesquite thickets and plains.

He soon found that ranch life in the Texas "wilderness" was not as expected. Riding the range was a lonesome and dangerous business. Being constantly alert for marauding Indians wore heavily. This was Comanche territory, a tribe known for their cruelty and acts of destroying their adversaries. No prisoners, no captives, remained alive for long. Encountering the savages was not infrequent. They came in small groups, 3 or 4 racing headlong into camp, scattering cattle requiring days to roundup. They would vanish into the thicket, quickly as they came. Sometimes one could get off a shot and bring one down, but Will found this was not wise. To kill an Indian resulted in the survivor turning back to rescue the victim and fight with a vengeance. The Comanche would not leave a comrade dead on the battlefield. Racing stirrup to stirrup, the warriors would straddle the victim on the ground, swoop and pick him up like playing a game. One best take cover and let them be.

Sometime Will would be gone from the ranch house and human association for extended periods. He had to adapt himself to coarse food of his own cooking, sleeping on the ground, and to many other hardships. His daily work consisted of driving cattle back on the home range, branding calves, running off strays, rounding up and counting grazing herds, and keeping a lookout for Indians, and rustlers. Will often smiled to himself as he recounted the legendary cowboy of the western frontier. "That on a fine day or night, few occupations in the western frontier was more cheerful, lively, and pleasant than that of the cowboy." But when the storm comes then his manhood and often his skill and bravery put to test. When the night is inky dark, and lightning's flashing its zigzag course across the heavens, and thunder jars the earth, and winds moan over the prairie, and electric balls dance from tip to tip of the cattle horns . . . , then the position of the cowboy on duty is trying . . . far more than romantic.

Will found that accumulating cattle required money and hired help. His ability to achieve a herd of his own was discouraging. His dream of trailing his own herd to Dodge City vanished. His restless nature prevailed, and he was motivated to seek out other opportunities, a more involved adventuresome occupation. He rode into Weatherford and pulled up in front of the Texas Rangers headquarters.

ASIDE:

The Ranger organization stood as a symbol of the law of the West, the protector of civilized society. The law was based on the theory that the cowman and the farmer had an inherent right to the land but the Mexican and the Indian did not. The role of the Texas Rangers in state law enforcement went through somewhat of an evolutionary process since the establishment of "ranging" companies in 1823. It's beginning was something of a Para-military force against the marauding and menacing Indians. The "ranging" man proved to be effective in clearing the way for white settlers' expansion westward. They did not practice discrimination between warring and peaceful Indians; they simply pursued the course of ridding the territory of all of them. This was the organization of the Texas Rangers.

Being a permanent law enforcing institution of the state, the rangers had access to the latest weapons invented and produced. Captain John Coffee Hays of Tennessee, first setup a permanent station for the rangers at San Antonio, in year 1840, they were equipped with the first six shooters, (1838), and later with the colt .44, in (1842), the second model released. At the battle of the perdenials, the first battle ever to use six shooters on mounted Indians 14 rangers engaged 70 Indians, and killed over 30 at this one skirmish. Texas rangers became national heroes.

The success of the rangers in eradicating the major threats by Indian tribes was also challenged by the Mexicans in the south during the 1840's and 1850's. The Texas rangers concentrated their efforts in border areas, on behalf of the new settlers harassing the Mexican residents who did not want to give up the land that belonged to them. The Texas revolution and the Mexican-American war provided justification for Rangers, in ridding the territory of thousands of Mexicans. When Texas attained statehood in 1845, all Mexicans residing in the new state boundaries were doomed to an existence of inequity, poverty, and mistreatment by ranger lawmen. The crime of these people was simply that they had been born Mexican and lived north of the Rio Grande River; for many, killing was instant, often whimsical, at the hands of the Texas rangers.

Will dismounted and tossed the reins over the hitching post. On the porch of the rangers' headquarters, languished three lanky men, one seated on the steps, one in a rocker, and one leaning against the door. A quiet, peaceful, picture of pure laziness; like lightning, lying dormant in a cloud, capable of striking in a burst of fury when ignited. These brave Indian fighters and scourge of the lawless, emoted a strange thrill in

Will. Just to be in their presence ignited a feeling and strong desire to be one of them.

They looked Will over without a greeting, or comment, eyeing him closely without being obvious. His slender 6'3" frame cut a striking figure. His single cold gray eye stared, unblinking, from a slit under the brim of a flat crowned floppy wool hat. The black eye patch was threatening. His countenance was strong and brooding, and his movements were noticeably easy, none of the horsemen's awkwardness in walking. He moved like the hunter he was. His shirt, once red, had faded to an undetermined rose; his vest was black cowhide, worn and scratched, and over his black jeans he wore fringy chaps, also black with tarnished honchos. He wore a tied down S & W Russian .44 six-shooter. "Hay Rip, come out here, you've gotta see this," one called. John Rip Ford, Captain of the Texas Ranger, ambled through the doorway and quietly looked Will over. He turned to stare at Jones. Will felt a sense of resentment at taking a subordinate position to his horse.

"Strange looking horse," Rip said. "What's his name?" "Jones" replied Will unsmiling. "That figures," said Ford. The others smiled. "What you up to fellow?" "Well, I didn't come here to discuss my horse. I want a job, that is I want to join your outfit or organization if you think well of it," Will drawled. Rip Ford had a strange premonition about Will and his horse, Jones. To perceive the real Will one had to see the two together, he and his wicked eye horse. The first and last impression was to avoid a confrontation with either, gunfight or horse race. The two exuded a confident air that they were winners and dare not lose.

Will relished over his first assignment. He was to work in the mineral wells area, and quickly found it mandatory to live up to the image of the Rangers. This, by enforcing the law mostly single-handed. Although he was only 20, the youngest ranger ever to join the organization, the rough hard life he was accustomed to, had worn off much of his youthful appearance. His hard sharp countenance and the tanned, weather-beaten skin, belied his youth. He smiled as he recalled the demonstration of his marksmanship with both the rifle and sidearm, "impressed the hell out of them" he mused.

Captain Rip Ford rode with Will on a number of routine patrols. When Will joined the ranger organization he was told they were closely allied with economic interest of the State, one of these being protecting the lives of the Anglo settlers. The Indians were raiding the settlers, driving off their herds, and capturing young children, who were taken westward to the staked plains, where they engaged in illicit trade with Mexican comancheros. General Sam Houston, president of Texas, was getting fed up with such lawlessness.

The rangers not only chased the Indians, but retrieved herds of cattle and horses stolen from the settlers. It was said that the Texas Ranger should be united with the federal service, pay them federal money and let them run all the Mexicans into the Rio Grande and all the Indians into the red river.

Will also soon found that the rangers could be counted on to create a situation where the white man could become rich, profiting from the hard life of the rangers. These protectors, were supported with money and influence. It was to the rancher's advantage that the ranger's image be enhanced as much as possible to counter any criticism that would be made about the ranger force to do his task. The ranger had complete freedom to be as ruthless as he wanted to be, the victims being mostly Indians and Mexicans.

ASIDE:

The Comanches stepped up their hit and run raids, throughout the 1800's and into 1876, in spite of treaties. The Indian's refused to enter the reservation set aside by the Texas legislature in 1854, consisting of 70,000 acres in two locations, Brazos River and the Clean Fork of the Brazos. This was pitifully small and half-heartedly received. Texas thought it generous and also felt the Indians were federal responsibility in the first place. Most of the Comanaches left the reservations and continued marauding. Peta Nocona, husband of Cynthia Parker, of Parker fort massacre fame, was killed by ranger Sul Ross in 1858; Nocona's son, Quanah Parker, now a 24 year-old warrior took command. Will Purdy was caught up in this rebellion, he had no knowledge of the Parker family massacre, and of 11 year old Cynthia being captured and raised by the Comanche to eventually become wife to Chief Nicoma. That Cynthia 24 years later was rescued by the Rangers, returned to her original family, but broken hearted at losing her own family. She died and was buried in Tarrant County. History tells us, her body was disinterred in 1958 and was buried beside that of her son Quanah, at the Fort Sill, Oklahoma reservation with full military honors. Such is Texas's history.

Will was compelled to methodically learn of the Comanche habits and their methods of warfare. The ranger companies met the Indian head on with such success the rangers became nationally famous. Still, coping with 1300 miles of frontier and the Indians hit-and-run tactics, was an insurmountable task. The swift and agile Indian ponies could carry the marauders miles away before news of their latest outrage could reach the rangers. Then, too, the Comanches were superior horsemen and could take a pony through thick brush that no white man could penetrate. This embarrassed the rangers and made them more determined to run the Comanches down and eradicate them.

Will encountered a ghastly experience near Palo Alto. He alone ran down and captured an Indian with stolen horses and found him covered with blood. He discovered that when Indians were being hotly pursued, they would shoot arrows into the horses they were driving to make them run.

In an effort to cover the 1300-mile frontier, comprising the Comanche area, the governor of Texas decided upon establishing a series of ranger post to be manned by "Minute-Men." Who, generally safeguarded life along the Texas frontier. They had considerable help, notably from the U. S. Cavalry. The rangers safeguarded Texans property like ordinary policeman, but there function went much farther. The rangers rode after the dreaded Comanche who held sway in the mineral wells, Weatherford area and northwest to Seymour, Guthers, Crowell, Cedar Lake and to the Palo Duro Canyon, at Amarillo. The Indian's chief occupation was raiding the Anglo American settlers driving off their live stock and capturing their children.

According to Rip Ford's briefing, in addition to the Indian menace, there was an on-going situation of lawlessness in the little cow town of Lobo, and in much need of being dealt with. Will relished the thought of getting this type of assignment.

Rip Ford gave Will a briefing on the Comanches. "There was never a more vicious scoundrel that infested the country than Quanah Parker, chief of the Comanche." The rangers focused on the day he would be brought to justice. The ability of frontier military commanders, who had often set out from Fort Concho, Texas with cavalry and infantry, chased the Indians for months at a time but rarely forced them into a decisive battle. The Comanches led by the cunning young chieftain, Quanah Parker, outwitted the troops in every faction of plains warfare. A Colonel McKenzie had some luck with the comancheros by destroying their trade goods, burning their wigwams, and raiding their campsites. Their illicit trading was eventually smashed, but McKenzie's victory did not quiet the Texas frontier. The Indians eventually met their defeat at Palo Duro Canyon when McKenzie took the entire herd of horses and slaughtered over 1500, leaving the Comanche afoot. The hide hunters had destroyed the buffalo, and their source of food gone. Quanah Parker capitulated and led his entire tribe to Fort Sill where they became incarcerated for life. The Texas frontier became safe for settlements and the era of the cattle barons was at hand.

CEDAR LAKE COUNTRY

Chapter Six

CEDAR LAKE—COMANCHE COUNTRY

According to Rip's briefing, the Indians of Cedar Lake seem to have ready access to military rifles. This was baffling, and Will Purdy was being sent on a special mission to get to the bottom of it. The whole area, from Lincoln County, New Mexico territory, to the Llano Estacada, was infested with the lawless. Be it renegade Comanches, comencheros, rustlers, or conniving enlistees stationed at the small garrison near the cow town of Lobo. Then too, don't count out the owners and operators of the Lobo's Den, a haven for crooks of all description, gamblers, whores, swindlers, gunmen, all feeding off the 10,000 dollar monthly payroll for the small fort. "Ah'm gonna have a field day and can't wait to get thar," Will mumbled to himself. "Maybe ah can't read or write, but I can shoot and Jones can outrun a frightened coyote, he mused. Hope Jones can turn himself into a camel, cause Rip said, water would be scarce. We'll make it."

Will was well apprised of the conditions around Cedar Lake. The west Texas settlers, be they ranchers or farmers, were outraged at the prevalence of the lawless; drovers registered complaints with the Governor. They were losing hundreds of cattle by taking the Cedar Lake short cut to Dodge City. The rustlers seemed to be well organized in disposing of their theft. The violence and depravity existing, generally, in the Lobo's Den covered to a large extent, the activity of the rustlers.

When Will and his horse, Jones, ascended the cap rock he could hardly believe his eyes. He had heard many tall tales of the great plains of Texas along with those of the Comanches who declared themselves "Lords of the Plains," how he thrilled at seeing it first hand. His first premonition of danger: "Lord, ah'm really exposed. No place to hide. . . ah can see for miles."

The plateau was like a flat top fortress. It brooded dark and solid against a wide blue cloudless sky. It was a citadel, two hundred miles long, one hundred fifty feet high. Along the plateau's rim, the gypsum cap rock gleamed like silver in the sun. It was a desert, a trackless waste. Nothing grew there but grass. The only water was alkali, poisoned by mineral salts. No one had ever mapped the plateau. It was considered deadly country and few dared to go there.

ASIDE:

In 1541 the Pueblo Indians, led by Francisco Vasquez de Coronado and 300 soldiers, had a chase across the top of the plateau. Mile after mile the Spaniards and their 600 pueblo slaves toiled across the plateau. It was level as a griddle and almost as hot. There was nothing, no trees, no boulders, no ridges or mountains to measure their progress. There were runs, but they were gouged into the surface of the plain, and invisible until one's horse teetered on the edge. The air shimmered and trembled incessantly. A raven in the distance would stretch and distort until it looked like a man approaching, giving the land the look of a place inhabited by phantoms. Groves and pools shimmered and beckoned, then vanished. The soldiers and Indians went days without seeing any shade. The grass, only inches high and burned a deep yellow color; closed after their horses passed. Almost a thousand men, their mounts and pack animals, left no more mark of their passing than a ship leaves in the ocean. So they cut saplings from the stunted cottonwoods and willows and staked their route with pole. Some of them stood years later. In time the plateau became known as El Llano Estacada, the staked plains.

Will struck out at sunrise to cover the remaining 40 miles to Lobo. On the way he crossed a noticeably well-traveled pathway, obviously the route of the cattle drovers bringing their herds up from Bandera and San Antonio, a short cut to the Kansas railheads.

For a while, Will followed the trail of the drovers before deciding to cut across the prairie to avoid a series of ravenes appearing on the surface. This turned out to be a tragic mistake. Jones stepped in a prairie dog hole and snapped his right front leg. He went down hard, throwing Will headlong into a prickly pear patch, painfully inflecting him with tiny thorns. The code of the range, in situations like this, was to relieve the horse of his pain. There is no recovery from a broken leg, and the horse is doomed to a slow death from starvation. Will's loyal and sturdy friend, the best one he had ever known, had to be put away. He removed his gear and saddle, and gently laid the blanket over Jonas' head. He lay still awaiting the inevitable. Will, ever cautious of impending danger, slowly removed his .44, placed his hat over the muzzle to muffle the noise, and sent Jones to his eternal pasture in the sky.

Will was shocked and sad, but being tested many times by the ravages of the frontier and its environ, he did not throw caution to the wind. He now faced a predicament that would further test his acumen for survival. Crossing the barren plain without encountering renegade Indians, and making it safely to Lobo, was indeed a challenge. Nevertheless, the muffled shot rendered to Jonas, tore the heart out of this seasoned Ranger, and he convulsed in emotions for an hour.

Will picked up his saddle and small amount of gear. Rangers traveled light. He calculated he had traveled at least half the distance to Lobo from his starting point. The next 20 miles could be made under darkness if need be.

Will made his way back to the drovers trail. It was facetious to think a cattle drive would come to his rescue, but he simply had nowhere to go. Right now he would almost welcome an Indian raid. However, he soon gathered his faculties, subdued his emotions, and struck out in the direction of Lobo. He stayed close to the trail and plodded westward, packing gear and saddle took its toll. By nightfall he was fairly exhausted and sought cover for rest. He believed he was within 10 miles of Cedar Lake, the birthplace of Chief Quanah Parker, their summer campground and burial site. Will's concern was getting around the lake without detection. His only chance was to do this under cover of darkness.

After negotiating the distance around Cedar Lake, the cow town of Lobo was another 10 miles west. He figured the final stretch was well off limits for Indians, especially in the daytime.

Will cut sagebrush and fashioned a cover for his daylight hide-away. There he sweltered until nightfall, before moving on. The white alkaline bed of Cedar Lake shimmered like silver in the night. The well-worn cattle trail looped around the southern end and on into Lobo. There a small garrison of mounted federal troops was stationed. He felt safe enough but took no chances of being detected. He muffled his spurs and covered the haunchos exposed on his saddle and chaps. These would reflect from the moonlight and alert an Indian whose gaze picked up any glint of movement. Marauding Comanches returning form a hunt could lurk in strange places. He could see their campfires dotting the small scrub, Cedar Islands in the waterless lake.

As he walked the final trek around the tip of Cedar Lake, he could not help but reflect on the plight of the Indians. Quanah's defeat opened the Texas western frontier for settlement. Settlers could live and exist without constant fear. Prior to the final curtain drawn down on the Comanches at Palo Duro Canyon. The small-unincorporated town of Lobo became a focal point for wagon train guides, drovers, and a destination for rustlers and gunslinger, whores, and gamblers.

The Indians of the Llano Estacada existed here when they could not have existed elsewhere. The army could not mount a campaign here: no water. The Comanches must have found a way to live without it. The army had a chronic complaint: the only way to do their mean varmints in is to trash them soundly, and the ones left will sorta take to you and mind their manners. But no! We have to stand at the border with our hat in our hand and wait for them to come out and play. The Comanches may be red-bellied savages, but they ain't stupid. They can figure out limits. Some way they can gage a carbines range and stay just outside that range. The army chased away the Indians but always they came back. The Texans would watch in fear and dread as the full Comanche moon rose in September when its brilliance washed the top of the trees, and bushes lapped against door jams and seeped light through cracks in shuttered windows. No one slept easy. And the settlers cursed the light.

The rangers were the curse of the Indians. They made cold camps and traveled fast and silently. No ranger could ever really understand how Indians felt about them or things. They were the uncertain creatures in God's creation. We took away their country, their means of support and broke there living habits. Introduced disease and decay among them, and for this they made war. Could anyone expect less? Such thoughts pervaded Will's mind. Also, he thought, men in Washington cynically blamed the Indian troubles on vengeful whites and profiteers, crooked freighters and contractors, and railroads, supplying the army. They pointed to the federal administration of Indian affairs, which was most certainly corrupt, and they accused the conquered confederacy of Texas of exaggerating reports of Indian raids. Chasing Indians gave federal occupying troops something to do besides harassing the Texans. They gave the Indians no thought once they had gotten their land from them.

Will walked on, the saddle hanging uncomfortable on his lean hip. He searched for some food, water, and energy.

So this was Quanah Parker's Country. The thought

occurred to him as long as there were young men like Quanah around, you could bet there would be war.

Traveling across the sagebrush prairie, approaching Cedar Lake, Will reflected upon the vast open range that dominated the landscape.

ASIDE:

Although the era of the great ranches on the open range blazed only briefly on our memory shelves, it colored forever the popular image of West Texas. The cattle drovers, turned cattle barons, the Texas rangers, curse of the Comanches, played a major role in taming the 1300 miles of Texas frontier.

Before Will loomed the enigma of Cedar Lake, the waterless alkaline creation spreading out ten miles or more in every direction. It lay like a sleeping giant in the vast acreage of lush grassland surrounding it. The placid response of nature's phenomenon concluded from the newcomer, its history of hardships, an environment of people living in dugouts and half dugouts. Cooking their food with cow chips and mesquite. The history of woman giving birth to large families and being mother, doctor, comforters and teachers to her children and any orphan that passed her door. Many were homesteaders who never lived out their term, then abandoned their shacks, a stark expose of the times. Surviving the times, the depression, the dust bowl; they drew their strength and courage from their perception of Christianity, Christianity as a life in the world, not as a voice crying in the wilderness; not as an idea in the air, but feet on the ground, undaunted, going God's way. These were the people of plain everyday goodness for which there is no substitute. History remembers them only for whom they were, not for what they did.

At daybreak, Will stepped upon the porch of the Lobo's Den. He passed his pack and saddle to the floor and pushed apart the swinging doors. Even at this early hour some human presence was visible. This was obviously the towns' only hangout. The soldiers had dubbed it "home of the coyote dung." A bedraggled lady of the night pushed a bottle and a glass at Will, "looks like you could stand a little of this, as well as a shave," she said unsmilingly. "We can supply whatever your soul can stand, even a bath with the works." "Sounds good to me," he replied. Then a voice behind him, "take off, Mag, get some sleep, and thanks for handling things last night, unexpected as they were." Will turned to find at arms length the prettiest lady he recalls having ever seen. A wholesome brunet, rosy cheeks, blue-eyed and a rounded figure stuffed firmly into a chambray shirt and blue jeans. Her small waist was circled by a black cartridge belt, minus holster. Strange, bullets but no gun or holster, yet adorned by pearl laden honchos. A large hand made buckle held the ends together. This is all it took to show off a figure. The envy of any gun-moll or ranchers daughter. Will wondered in this fleeting moment, which one she was. She smiled at Will, invited him to sit, and motioned to the kitchen. "Bring some food . . . two hungry folks out here. They sat and coffee came immediately. "Couldn't help but notice your saddle and tack on the porch, trouble with your horse, obviously." "You've got that right", replied Will, wide-eyed and marveling at her beauty. Then he thought quickly to himself, been too long since I've been around a creature like this . . . try not to be obvious.

She proffered her hand, "names Utoka Jett. I run this place. Welcome to Lobo, and the Lobo's Den. Not much else around here." "Why was last night so unusual, as you mentioned to Meg?" She said, "because no one got killed," and laughed. "That kinda place, is it?"

"What are you doing here if it's that kind of place?" Will asked, then quickly apologized. "Ain't none of my business, forgive me for asking." "Well I could've made the same mistake by asking the same of you. I don't even know your name?" "Name's Will Purdy, and I'm on the lamb from the Texas

Ranger organization." "I won't ask why," she responded. "You figure you won't get a straight answer?" "You got that right." Will looked straight into the pools of blue. "I'm a Ranger deserter, had to beat it because I had to kill one of them for stealing my horse. The government is mad as hell. They are all after me," he said grimly. "What are you planning to do out here?" "Don't know just yet, maybe return to my old profession . . . a hired gun. I'm still good at that." Utoka appeared rather cool after this brief conversation, and that's the way Will wanted it. After all, how does he know who she is? Part of the gang around here? Who knows?

All I need is her confidence and interest and friendship. Can't believe she is one of the crooks in the pot. But, how is it she runs this place? Suppose she owns it? Much raced thru Will's mind as they polished off a good breakfast of steak and eggs and lots of hot coffee. Will felt like a new man. Now for a good bath and a shave and a horse. Utoka announced she could do it all for him. An hour later he met her at the bar and walked her to the livery stable nearby.

"The first three you see are mine. Take your pick. They are all good and fast. I've raced them all and we always win. Shades of Jones, thought Will, and he couldn't wait until he had thrown Jones' saddle on the striking bay he selected.

Will took a room topside of the Den and for the next 3 or 4 days hung out pretty much to himself.

He continued to be fascinated by Utoka's beauty, and he floundered in her presence. He wondered if she noticed his awkwardness. I'm seeing too much of her, got to get my mind on something else, and get busy. Rip's gonna be wanting a report from me before long. Like 6 months or so, and at this method of operating, time is going to slip away. Golly, she's a beauty! Will was smitten, and in for a sucker. Utoka Jett was a plant and of the type he would never have contemplated.

Will decided to observe things at the Lobo's Den from evening to evening. He was curious of the patrons who showed, and what they did. Standing alone at the far end of the bar, Utoka eased up beside him. He was startled, then gained composure and asked her to join him for a drink. "Over here," she said, motioning to an empty table.

They sipped at their drink, and Will attempted a nonchalant poise, uncomfortable as it was; how do you suddenly become somebody you're not, he thought to himself. He had to play out a role to remain incognito, his identity became known in Lobe as a Texas Ranger it would be Katie bar the door. He half-seated, half-layed in the barrel chair, long legs stretched out, and squinted at a longhaired guy by the window. The long hair began picking a tune on a guitar "whose that hombre with the guitar and long hair?" "Name's Pelham Ware, come in here about six months ago." Utoka advised "keeps hanging around and pretends to drink, but I happen to know he doesn't," she said. "What da you suppose he's up to? Gotta make a living somehow, who knows, doesn't bother anybody, and no one seems to pay him any mind." "Can he sang with his pickin?" "Go ask Him, he'd probably feel complimented coming from you. He seems to like cowboys and that you ain't," she smiled. "You got that right, and I need a job."

Pelham Ware cast a wary eye upward at the tall lanky cowman standing over him. "What you want?" he asked, continuing to strum the instrument. "Can you sing?" "What do you wanna hear?" he replied. "Forget it," said Will. He returned to his table. Utoka had disappeared. Within minutes, two characters accosted him at the table. "Who do you think you are to come in here and start shining up to my girlfriend?" One snarled at him, "Yeah," said the other, "he was over picking on the guitar player, too." Will realized these two guys wanted to pick a fight with him. I think I'll just accommodate them, got to get a reputation around here. If I have to buy it the hard way, so be it. He kicked the table away, sprang to his feet, drew his .44 quicker than the eye could detect, and ordered the two "get the hell outa here and don't come back." The saloon patrons were astounded. A stranger ordering out the two most notorious gunmen in town; Pelham Ware moved quickly and silently behind the bar, and waited. The two had vanished momentarily, and then re-entered the Den. The swinging doors burst and Ware let the lead man have it, Will took the other one. He walked over to Pelham, "why did you get involved?" "I just wanted to keep you around so you could hear me sing", he replied. Utoka heard the commotion, but didn't see it. She burst from a closed door and went straight to Will, eyes flashing a touch of anger. "Who are you anyway? You have just finished off the fastest gun in town." "Who did they work for, maybe I can get a job," he smiled. She spun away. Pelham flashed him a big grin, two men came to the bar and offered to buy him a drink. I think they'll remember me now, and he strode the full length of the saloon and out the swinging doors, mounted and rode north.

Still wondering who Utoka Jett is, and that guitar player is mighty handy with a gun. He jogged on, no destination, just getting out of town.

At dust, Will made camp, and stretched out on the lush grass. His horse grazed contentedly nearby. He dozed off. The stars came out. A Texas moon on the prairies; a Texas night with all the stars ablaze is something to behold. The sky appears close enough to reach up and be touched.

Will's horse whinnied, another horse approaching. It had a rider, a woman dressed in soft tanned buckskin. The matching hat also matched the long flowing hair that framed as pretty a face as Will had ever seen. She pounced to the ground, lithe and stealthy. Will stood up and stretched himself showing no interest. "Vashti's the name," she smiled and offered her hand. He took it like the gentleman he was, but with his left hand she noticed that, and flashed another smile. "Heard about you, you just polished off two of my hands, hope you are looking for a job because I need replacements." "That I am." "You've got it," she said matter-of-factly. "Come, saddle up, and follow me."

She jumped into the stirrup and straddled the great Zebra Dunn. He snorted and leaped forward. She sat him like a pro. "What you waiting for?" she shouted impatiently. Will was moved out of his moment of fascination and quickly threw the saddle on his mount. "Take off; I'll be right behind you." He was relishing an opportunity to test his new horse. She left in a burst of speed, with Will quickly closing the gap.

MADAM

Chapter Seven

MADAM OF THE LOBO'S DEN

UTOKA JETT

Utoka Jett was born and raised in the little Georgia village of Sycamore, in the early 1840's. The village of Sycamore was designated as the perfect stopover for the "Red Line" stagecoach, operating out of Atlanta, with connections all the way from Chicago and south to the Florida panhandle and on to Texas. The little village was nameless until a careless passenger wondered too far into the woods and found himself scrambling up a prominent Sycamore tree, to escape the wrath of a she-black bear. This incident became better known than the stage stopover, thus the name, Sycamore, Ga. Better known than the name, "Sycamore", however, was the female stagecoach attendant dubbed "Axel Grease Annie." She was the daughter of old Tom Jett, owner and operator of the stop over facility, which maintained fresh replacement teams, a restaurant and a bunkhouse in case of emergency needs for sleep-over, seldom used. Ma Jett died when Annie was 12 and Annie took over ma's duties, which was wheel inspection when the stagecoach wheeled in for service. The service was normally limited to applying a goodly smear of axel grease to the screaming wheels. Passengers could expect to see a wholesome teenager flying out of the shed with a bucket in one hand and a paddle made of sycamore. Annie's dad had fashioned a prod-pole into a lift action device enabling Annie to remove the wheel in quick order, apply the grease and have the coach readied by the time pa had the teams ready for exchange. Axel grease Annie was a doll. To observe her shapely body encased in jeans and open throated shirt accentuated a jovial face, brilliant smile, and raven hair cropped short and snobbish. Her throaty laugh and the lilt in her voice caught the attention of passengers. They paused as they unloaded for a quick bite to eat, and took in Annie's vivacious welcome. All the time she was preparing to smear the axel greases, thus her nickname.

Annie was also known for her expertise with a rifle and side arm. With some urging she would occasionally display her marksmanship to the bantering men folk on the stage. At the age of 16, Tom realized she was a heartthrob to every buckaroo who came Sycamore way, and he likened her to honey attracting the proverbial black bear. He formulated guidelines to shelter her from the more rambunctious cowboys in the area. This did not set too well with Annie, and she often dwelled upon her future and what possibly did it hold for her.

It was a hot day in August when the gaudy Red and Yellow striped stagecoach lurched around the bend of the Red-clay dusty Georgia road. Redline coach service from Atlanta to Texas, Sycamore, Georgia being the first stopover. Pa and Ma Jett operated the station for years, until ma died from sheer exhaustion and stress. By the time of her demise, Annie had reached full womanhood, and what a woman she was. The raven-haired beauty, a genuine Georgia peach, greeted the stagecoach, and went about performing duties Pa had taught her. On this day in August it was hot. The driver swung the six horse tandem hook-up into the open lot, and wiped the clay dust and sweat from his brow. The teams showed exhaustion, and the steam rising from their sweltering hides, dripping in mud, added to the nausea of Annie and Pa as they unhitched and prepared horsepower exchange.

Axel Annie was too busy with her duties to notice the handsome middle age passenger staring at her. All others had vacated the stage for the dining hall. This man obviously by dress of Chicago vintage, sat motionless, perspiration forming small trickles thru red clay dust on his face, and then Annie smiled. He smiled back. "Did I hear right?" He asked. "They called you Axel Grease Annie?" "That's right, been called that for years, kind'a my job, helping Pa since Ma died." "You ever thought of moving on to a different life?" "Why?" "Well, doesn't seem to be much here in Sycamore for you, is there?" "Depends." Then she turned her pools of blue and appeared to look right through him. "Where pray tell me, would I go, and leave Pa to die like Ma, exhausted, stressed, and starved? I'm a Georgia girl, and devoted to my lot. Sure I've known since I was a kid the short end of the stick had my name on it; I'm doing the best I know how." "Now you better get to the dining room or you're going to travel hungry", she blustered emotionally. She turned to let down the "greased wheel," and turned, he thought, sadly away.

Shortly the stage was re-boarded and readied for the next leg of the dusty journey. The "Chicago" man approached Annie and handed her his business card. "I will see you again, sometime, somewhere, somehow." She offered her hand, he squeezed it tenderly, and a strange sensation surged through sensory faculties as if it could be true. The stage lurched forward, away and gone. Annie showed the card to pa. It reads "Allen Pinkerton detective agency—Investigation Specialist" Chicago, Ill. Etc. etc.

ASIDE:

Allan Pinkerton was an Englishman from Great Britain who came to America in 1840. He established his detective Agency in Chicago and eventually became famous for his expertise in breaking up an organized train robbery syndicate, including the James brothers and associated gangsters.

Two years elapsed from the initial meeting of Allan and Annie in Sycamore, Ga. He had pursued his mission of Investigative Service with the cattleman's association in Texas who were outraged at the lawlessness being perpetrated upon the pioneer ranchers. Cattle rustling had become a profession, and ranchers needed help. The Texas Ranger force was limited and highly engaged in fighting renegade Comanche Indians who continually engaged in raiding settlers. This was a situation fortunate to the goals of the Pinkerton Agency, famous for the break-up of the railroad frauds of Chicago. Allan hung out for months in the little cow town of Lobo, Texas, center of the south plains cattle country. Other than a brothel and saloon named Lobo's Den, and a small garrison of federal cavalry, there was not much to see. It was here, however, that Allan perceived the core of the cattle rustling activity existed. The lush grasslands of Cedar Lake attracted drovers bringing thousands upon thousands of longhorns up from San Antonio and to the railheads at Dodge City and Abilene, Kansas. Herds were original targets for organized rustlers, who stashed away their illicit loot on leased land, and created a magnet for raiding adjacent ranchers. They melded their herds in with those being trailed thru Lobo to Dodge. Allan had a hunch that he could ferret out the devious means employed to carry out the rustler's schemes. He needed axel Annie (God, what a name, but he would change that) Allan became almost fanatical in projecting plans upon his return to Chicago. He immediately dispatched his most able associate to find Axel Annie and get her to Lobo, Texas and on the job. Pelham Ware, the associate, so designated, was himself an expert in disguising. The most favorable pose being that of a vagabond troubadour, going about the country with a guitar slung across his back, singing cowboy songs. Pelham headed for Georgia.

Josh Epps was the new owner of the Lobo's Den bought for the purpose of bringing Vashti home to take care of him in his paralyzed state. Vashti was ecstatic over her new home as it placed her right in the center of her rustling activities. Josh was too naive to have any inkling of her clandestine activities. He was literally infatuated by her charm and beauty. He vowed that one day she would grace his ranch headquarters, now under construction. As his caregiver she became known far and wide as the baroness of the Lazy "V". He would bide his time. Then along came Pelham Ware and Axel Annie posing as a team of saloon operators and looking for a lease option to buy the Lobo's Den. Just what Josh had hoped for? He made a bargain offer to sell. Ware could not refuse and had no intentions to do so.

ASIDE:

Ware and Annie took over the Lobo's Den; she was introduced as Utoka Jett, madam from Georgia. Ware stayed in the background posing as a good for nothing vagabond, belting out songs and strumming his guitar. Actually, Pelham was a pretty good entertainer, but he took a lot of abuse from the heavy drinkers.

In the ensuing two years since Annie met Allan Pinkerton. She lost her father in a nasty accident. Old Tom Jett got entangled in the traces of a runaway team while changing out the teams. He was dragged to his death. Annie found herself alone and not capable of keeping up the Way Station. She sold out and during the transfer to the new owners she had agreed to stay a while. But not for long, Pelham Ware appeared and within days they were traveling to Texas.

In their flight to Texas, Utoke and Pelham Ware were run-down by confederate cavalryman, but Utoka's southern charm embarrassed the cavalrymen to ever have such thoughts that she and her "wounded husband" could have any connection with the north. They escaped to Adobe Walls on the Canadian River (Texas side) and then to Lobo, Texas and the plains cattle country.

Utoka was quick to learn the trade. Her raven-haired beauty was even more charming than the waxen haired blond bombshell of Vashti. Both clashed from the beginning. Utoka called Vashti's bluff by strapping on a pearl handled .38 and ordering her off the property. Vashti, proficient in her own right with her Russian Smith & Wesson revolver, froze in awe at the great beauty before her. Two of Josh's men stepped in to prevent a murder and coached Vashti to her horse and sent her home to Josh. Enemies were created then and there, and an eventual showdown was obvious.

Utoka soon found herself in a precarious position. The town of Lobo, near the Comanche burial ground of Cedar Lake became a focal point for wagon train guides, a destination for adventurers and pioneering settlers in the early 1800's. It served as a gathering place for trail drovers. The town became a recruiting center for Mexican vaqueros, gunslingers, and hired guns of the cattle baron's. The Lobo's Den, formerly known as the Flat, was a den of iniquity; of the 50 or more women in Lobo it was doubtful you could find a single virtuous one. The den was rife with gamblers, whores, thieves, and cattle rustlers. The only "watering hole" for miles and miles across the staked plains.

The "Flat", owned and managed by Vashti Epps, now abandoned in exchange for a grand wedding to one Josh Epps, largest cattle baron on the Texas plains. Vashti was now the baroness of the Lazy "V", and let everyone know of her power and authority. Utoka soon learned Vashti was thought to be in cahoots with the most organized band of rustlers ever known to exist. The ranchers, were outraged, and had requested the governor to send Texas rangers to assist, but apparently no one ever showed.

Not long after Utoka's arrival with the young vagabond guitar player named Pelham Ware, a young "one-eyed" gunman appeared in the Lobo's den and impressed her as a likely asset to break-up the lawless, only to find he was on the lamb from the law himself. His name was Will Purdy. During his short stay he had killed one of Vashti's hired guns, and lo and behold she had hired Purdy to work for her. However, the war got him. He was recruited for General Sibley's western expedition. Wonder whatever happened to him, she thought.

Before the war came to an end, there appeared a handsome young-gun, obviously a deserter from the confederacy. He hung around awhile, ever on the alert, and Utoka became quite fond of him. His name was Bat Morgan. Not long after his arrival he engaged in buffalo hide hunting and became quite wealthy. In fact he built another emporium next to the Lobo's Den and merged the two into a thriving classy dance hall and gaming house. Bat and Utoka co-mingled their professional pursuits, with guarded attitude, neither trusting the other.

The war came to a close. The Lobo's Den seems to catch every veteran drifter in west Texas. They were a motley, unhappy, restless breed, dangerous killers of every sort. Utoka was nervous of her status. Pinkerton had engaged her to become active in the cattle rustler break-up. She feared for Bat who had no compunctions against flaunting his wealth, yet Bat boasted of security behind an armada of rugged buffalo hunters who had proven their loyalty more than once. She wondered about Will Purdy. She needed him.

BATTLE OF GLORETTA PASS

Chapter Eight

FATAL EXPEDITION

GLORETTA PASS
(Gettysburg of the West)

Will cantered into town, his sleek bald face horse tuggin at the reins. He had a job and a connection the Ranger organization had hoped for. He sensed something strange going on at the Lazy "V". There seem to be tension, men at the bunkhouse appeared on guard. No joviality, pranks, or rivalry displayed normally found in bunkhouses. Oh well, maybe they don't like strangers. His gunning down one of the hired guns could have put them on edge. What about the boss-man, named Josh Epps. He saw neither hair nor hide of him. Only Vashti flittering about, in and out; and when he cantered by her he tipped his hat and smiled. She merely stared with a quizzical expression. Where could he be going this early in the morning, doesn't he know he's suppose to work?

At the Lobo's Den, Will noticed a small gathering of people listening to the talk of two men sitting on their horses. Both riders appeared strangely familiar. He pulled up and eased around behind them, stopping just in earshot of their words. He pulled his hat low over his eyes. Anybody would single him out with the eye-patch exposed.

One man was vocalizing loudly on the plight of the confederacy, and on the part the state of Texas was expected to play. That the war was going poorly for the south's cause; that the federals had at the on-set blockaded the eastern seaports cutting off much needed supplies and ammunition from Europe. Jefferson Davis had sounded the alarm. Texas and the entire confederacy were in jeopardy, unless a second port of entry was established on the west coast of the pacific, California, and Oregon. President Davis had commissioned an expeditionary force to secure these ports of entry. A mounted infantry was being formed to include a contingent of Texas rangers, under the command of General H. H. Sibley. Sibley was considered the foremost strategist in the army. Sibley needed men, and needed them now. "That's our mission. We urge you to sign up."

Intently, Will listened, rangers signing up, a far cry from his present mission chasing Indians and subduing the lawless. When there is a war going on, things get charged up. No question about it, Rip Ford would expect him to join his friends and associates to carry out this critical expedition. He set out to find Utoka.

ASIDE:

There was compelling evidence, convincing the most brilliant military strategist and civilian planners of the confederacy that capturing the west would mean ultimate southern victory, and to that end they devoted their limited resources.

Jefferson Davis certainly believed it; he assigned great importance to the campaign as evidenced by the men he assigned to carry it out. Henry Hopkins Sibley, one of the most able and competent officers in the southern military, and other southern leaders, were equally convinced that victory in the west would solve two of the most pressing problems of the confederacy. A lack of ready cash, a crippling shortage of goods, and deep-water seaports from which to carry out essential commerce with other nations. They believed that successfully conquering the west would make it possible for the south to ultimately defeat the union. From Texas west to California, the country was unincorporated as states; it was strictly of territory status. To bring this vast area with its abundant resources into the confederacy would be a victory of untold proportions to its cause. With approximately 40 vessels, the union was successful in shutting down 3500 miles of confederate coast and 189 harbors. When Lincoln announced the blockades, Jefferson Davis was faced with a problem.

The ranger recruiter pulled Will aside and advised that Rip Ford had sent a special message for him. Will was to set aside his assignments for the time being, and report to San Antonio immediately and join the Ranger contingent of General Sibley's army of Texas volunteers. That this westward campaign superseded all other ranger activity for the welfare of the state. That it would be a thrilling change of pace, and that Rip Ford was considering joining up as soon as he could negotiate a release from Ranger headquarters.

Will had one last evening with Utoka Jett. He told her briefly of his new job at Vashti's ranch. Utoka gasped, but made no remark. He told her good-bye, "I'll be back, don't know when, but I'll be back."

Will got a further briefing on the western campaign, while accompanying the ranger recruiters on their return to San Antonio. The briefing went like the following:

The union's strategy was to starve the South into submission by blockading its harbors, cutting off much needed trade and resources. One of the first reactions to Fort Sumter was Lincoln announcing the blockade. The South's only alternative was to find new harbors that could not be shut down by the North. These existed only in the two newest states in North America, California and Oregon.

There was not much between California and Texas to slow down the invaders. New Mexico territory was sparsely populated by farmers of Mexican descent, who harbored strong hatred of the U.S., which had wrested the land from Mexico in the war of 1846-49. The Colorado territory was scarcely settled; also Mormons who hated the U.S. government settled Utah territory. Oregon had only a few settlers, and California was filled with gold miners from both north and south. It was estimated there were 100,000 southerners in California who would not resist a confederate invasion. Success from the invasion appeared to be a walk in the west.

Actually this line of thinking or reasoning was arrogant. The New Mexicans had even deeper hatred for Texas than that for the U.S. after the Mexican-American war of 1846-49. Texas began to award big chunks of New Mexico land to the Texas veterans. The land grants were illegal and unspecific. Texas soldiers began arriving in New Mexico and laying claims to land, which was already owned, and being farmed by New Mexico residents. The Texans and their long rifles drove away the residents and the hatred for Texas grew stronger. All this history was ignored by the confederacy and was lulled into false security of the invasion being welcomed.

The capture of gold in California and Colorado would have made it possible for the confederacy to purchase all their needed supplies abroad. Most of all, the conquest of the west would add to the prestige of the confederacy and enhance possible recognition by all of Europe. Such recognition would have brought England and France into the war against the north, and it would win the struggle from the south. Such was the grandiose scheme of the confederacy.

Will rode directly to San Antonio reaching his destination on the third day out from Lobo. The gift horse from Utoka performed like a dream, the kind of horse admired by the cavalry. Will hoped he would not be separated from this fine piece of horseflesh; wishful thinking.

Will had no contact with Rip Ford, but found that Rip had preceded him to General Sibley's quarters. However, two days after his enlistment he received a handwritten note requesting his presence for dinner and a conference. Will was impressed with the handsome aggressive young general Sibley. He could easily perceive why Sibley was chosen to head the expedition. His powers of persuasion were dominate. "You may be taking a cut in pay to join the army," Sibley said to Will. "But if you have joined up just for the money you have joined for the wrong reason." "Money is no object in my case," Will responded. "It really is not about pay, is it?" Sibley went on: "It is about forces of evil, it is about saving our country, protecting our wives and children. It is about saving the south and the state of Texas from evil aggression."

By August 1861 Sibley was in San Antonio raising and training his western expeditionary forces. By early September nearly 5000 men were undergoing training. They had the best equipment available. Sibley could get anything he wanted. His was to be an elite unit undertaking a mission critical to the survival of the south.

The entire 4th regiment, with it's contingency of Texas rangers, marched into Fort Bliss, El Paso, Texas in January 1862. They began their ill-fated invasion of the west. They had with them between 300 & 400 supply wagons; eighty cannons, and an undetermined number of caissons and closed carriages. Sibley's western expeditionary force had five thousand horses and mules, and close to 4000 soldiers. In May, less than 5 months later, general Sibley stumbled back into Texas with seven wagons, 36 horses and mules and a total of 600 to 1500 men. Everything was lost.

General Sibley had led his volunteers into New Mexico, 3700 strong, and engaged in a number of insignificant skirmishes of the hit-and-run sort. In March of 62' one of the major fights of the war in the west took place at Glorretta Pass, near Santa Fe. A Major Chivington, an itinerant preacher in civilian life, from Denver, with 400 men scrambled over the mountain, scaling a steep wall, and descended upon the parked confederate wagons, took 60 of them complete with supplies at Apache Canyon and destroyed everything. Two confederate officers and 15 men were taken prisoner, one of whom was

Will Purdy, who went down under an onslaught of Major Chivington's rifleman. Will was wounded in three parts of his body by their bayonets.

General Sibley was forced to retreat to Santa Fe, and the southern invasion of the far west came to an end.

Will was left behind; a prisoner of the federal forces now occupying Santa Fe. He remained there in a small open stockade, and a small lean-to hospital tent, for two and a half years, before being released on an exchange of prisoners. Will had endured the winters of 1862 and 1863. Food supplies were short and the hospitalized prisoners gravely neglected. Many died from exposure and malnutrition. Will's rugged out door life fortified him with resistance to the bitter cold.

Will returned to the confederate troops at Fort Bliss and later to his old 4th regiment at Palacious, Texas where he served out the remaining days of the war.

The Ranger organization was outraged at the disgraceful leadership of General H. H. Sibley. Only a small percentage of the original ranger lancers survived the battle of Gloretta Pass. The worst of all was the tragic retreat across thousands of miles of arid and desolate land of the west.

Why the lopsided victory? The Texans pride was devastated. Historians agreed there was a difference existing between the federal forces and those of the rebels. It was found that when men are fighting off invaders they will fight more vicious in protecting their families and homes than will the invaders. In the western expedition, the rebels were the invaders. Too, it is good that the Texans had gone a little soft when recruited. Many who stayed in Texas and fought with General Hood distinguished themselves; those who signed on with Sibley mostly recruited in San Antonio and may have chosen Sibley thinking the expeditionary force would see little action and suffer but few casualties. Result, they may have been more reluctant to exert themselves in battle. It is possible that by joining Sibley's army some men were deliberately avoiding what they thought would be tough fighting in favor of a simple walk through the park.

The Coloradoans, under Major Chivington, the minister of the gospel, were recruited from rough and tumble gold mining camps of the Rockies. These men were used to hardships, struggle, living by their gun. They hunted in order to eat. They fought to protect their claims and because they were the type of men who would leave their home and go into the mountains alone to seek their fortunes, the so-called Pike Peaker's were not the sort to be easily cowed. They were accustomed to fighting to stay alive, and they were pretty good at it.

The Coloradoans, Pike's Peakers, soundly thrashed the Texans and sent them crying all the way home. Their pride had taken a serious beating. Many deserted and went to the gold fields of California, rather than face the humiliation of their home folks.

The Ranger organization petitioned for the court marshal of Gen. Sibley; maintaining that not once did he make a single decision in battle, simply because he was drunk. Although an experienced administrator, Sibley was a week strategic planner and a poor leader of men, who was even accused of cowardice in time of crisis. Moreover, he was often in poor health and had become addicted to the drink. That he was described as a "walking whisky keg."

President Lincoln didn't go there to make a speech; Mathew Brady didn't photograph the battle, Walt Whitman didn't write a poem about it, Colorado didn't even have a state to secede or stay with the union, just an outpost in the Kansas territories. The region and the battle were ignored by the rest of the world. The "Gettysburg of the west" may have saved the union, but is destined to remain mostly hidden in the annals of history.

The battle of Gloretta Pass, March 26-28, 1862 perhaps was the turning point in the war. Had Sibley succeeded, and by rights should have done so, the results of the War Between the States could have been decidedly different.

Anyway, this historical event is source for a tall tale.

CIVIL WAR ATROCITIES
AWOL CONDITIONS
DESERTERS
REBELS WITH A CAUSE

Chapter Nine

REBELS WITH A CAUSE

Bat Morgan was born in 1845 in a small room, a part of the Wild Card Saloon, Dodge City, Kansas. His mother, Hazel, operated the saloon. Prior to becoming heavy with child she had planned selling her business, but circumstances compelled her to take a different direction. A professional gambler by the name of Shane Morgan came to Dodge City with the law hot on his heels. Hazel befriended him, and they became partners in the gamblers-saloon operation. They operated the Wild Card Saloon for 15 years, until Bat had reached the age of 16. Bat witnessed the death of his mother and stepfather. They were caught in a shoot-out in a crossfire brawl. Bat left Dodge a grim and broken hearted kid. Within a year he was caught up in the War Between the States. Bat had traveled out of Dodge into Tennessee where he joined a wagon train, destination Mississippi and Alabama. In Gatlinburg Bat encountered a family in need of a teamster to handle one of the two family wagons enroute to Mississippi. Roland and his wife, Artie and daughter Etta. Artie was driving one of the two wagons and the strain was too much for her.

Roland was looking for help. The six-day ordeal had been too much for the two and he was seeking a driver to relieve his wife. Bat made known his interest in traveling south and was immediately hired to handle one of the Tucker wagons. He was advised the Tuckers were in the cotton mill and compress business in Corinth. Bat recognized the association with the Tuckers as possible opportunity for employment. He eagerly looked forward to the 300-mile trip, which would take them south by southwest into the heart of the cotton country. He had heard of big cotton plantations, worked by slave labor and overseen by aristocratic southern gentlemen. The prospects of becoming involved were exciting. He scurried about the wagons, cared for the horses, ran errands, and assisted every way possible to assure acceptance by the young and inexperienced Tuckers. He especially became fond of little Etta, a delightful twelve-year-old who shadowed his every move. They shared the high seat on the Conestoga and she giggled at Bat's expertise in cracking the long-tailed split-end rawhide whip.

They experienced five grueling days out of Gatlinburg and as they neared Chattanooga, Artie Tucker became deathly ill. Pneumonia had set in two days prior to coming in contact with medical assistance. She died and was buried in Chattanooga. Roland and daughter Etta were devastated over their loss. To avoid further endangering the life of Etta, Roland decided to abandon the wagons to the custody of the local livery stable and proceed to Corinth by train. Bat was heartbroken over the tragic occurrence and the loss of an expectant opportunity, as well as losing the companionship of little Etta.

Bat shook off his disappointment, left the wagon train, and rode alone south towards Gadsden, Alabama. He took the well-worn trails along Lookout Mountain, often resorting to shortcuts along Bill Wills River, camping alone. Being familiar with river life, he sought and found employment with a fur and pelt company. He spent the remainder of the winter trapping and hunting. When the winter thaw was underway and spring at hand, he moved on to Decatur, Alabama where he hired on as lumberjack, working the mountainous forest of northern Alabama. Here he remained for about a year, at which time his longing to see Roland Tucker and daughter Etta pressured him to leave and ride to Corinth.

In Corinth, the name of R. Tucker and Son was well known. The company was Corinth's largest employer, doing business of processing and warehousing thousands of bales of cotton through the compress. Young Tucker was delighted to see Bat and promptly prevailed upon Roland Senior to bring Bat into their employment. The Civil War was heating up and Mr. Tucker realized good able-bodied men may come into short supply due to enlistments and the conscriptions. Mr. Tucker was active in seeking exemptions for cotton mill workers as an essential occupation to the war effort. He later secured that status for his employees.

Bat renewed acquaintance with Etta. She had blossomed into a beautiful southern belle. He saw her often and he worked long hours and enthusiastically at his job. Bat learned the business and became proficient in the details of the operation of the compress and warehousing activity. He observed the marketing procedures and accompanied both Roland, Jr. and father on field surveys to gage cotton production and drum up business from the ginners. Mississippi was the most important cotton producing State in the entire Confederacy. Bat learned that the farms were not embodied in huge plantations, as he had envisioned. In fact, only twenty percent of the farm operators were planters owning 50 or more slaves, and as much as five hundred acres. The yeoman farmers of less than two hundred acres numbered sixty to seventy percent of Mississippi white population and had few, if any, slaves. More than half the farmers owned no slaves. This fact puzzled Bat in that all seemed to be anxious to defend the confederacy and its principle of slavery. The increase in the States population from 1830 to 1860 came from immigration from older southern states. As a result, 83% had been born in the South and only 5% in the North, or foreign birth, thus, the loyalty to the Confederacy.

The battle for Mississippi opened in 1862 along side the Tennessee River at Shiloh Church, just north of Corinth. On May 30, 1862, the Confederate Army evacuated Corinth. As the war progressed, cotton and other war materials came into such demand it was obvious Bat's exempt status was safe. The turmoil connected with economy was frightening. The war was costing Mississippi mightily. Slaves had fled from owners as union armies approached. Some 17,000 blacks had joined union forces. The war was devastating Mississippi's economy, social and governmental institutions. Outlook for the future was dim.

Although life was not pleasant for a young man not in uniform, Bat, through the urging of the senior Tucker, remained on the job protected from the horrors of the Civil War by an "exempt status." The confederate forces were plagued with deserters and dissenters, and anyone appearing to be AWOL was a strong suspect and a candidate for serious punishment.

Bat stayed close to his job and employment responsibilities for another year, but soon was caught up in a series of circumstances that had a serious impact on his life and his future.

The war was going badly for the confederates. Battle weary veterans were returning home with or without leave. Rounding up deserters became full time assignments for some confederate cavalry units. The atrocities perpetrated on captured deserters were horrible and despicable. Often trials were omitted, or even the taking of prisoners was abandoned. Rather, examples of cruel treatment were relied upon in an attempt to discourage desertions. Bat's personal encounter with this situation was excruciating. On a frosty night in February 1863, Bat had dropped Etta at her parent's home on the outskirts of Corinth, and was returning to his quarters near the mill. He met Jerry a good friend in service leading his lame mount. They decided to leave the horse with an accommodating neighbor until morning, whereupon Jerry and Bat returned to Etta's by buggy. As they approached the house, two confederate cavalrymen bore down on them, wrestled them from the buggy seat, and in spite of their pleading to show identification, killed Jerry with a blast from two pistols. They turned on Bat; Etta came screaming from the house. Bat managed to show his exempt status and was freed. The cavalrymen claimed two deserters were reported in the area and galloped away. Bat removed from Jerry's pocket the furlough authorization he never had a chance to show. He had been mistakenly murdered in cold blood by the war-toughened and heartless confederate cavalrymen. This experience embittered Bat on the Confederacy. After attending to the funeral for Jerry, and efforts to console Etta, he rode out of Corinth on Jerry's horse, hoping unrealistically to track down the two cavalrymen responsible for Jerry's death. Little did he realize how ineffective his efforts would be and the careless attitude of the cavalry unit to which they belonged.

Bat's quest took him to Meridian, Mississippi where he intended to contact the commander of the 7th Mississippi regiment. There he again encountered a comparable experience relating to desertion. He was accosted by a group of horsemen, some in uniform, and some in civilian dress. They lashed him to a tree and demanded explanation and proof of positive identification. These men were all deserters and had suspected Bat, a young man in civilian clothes attempting to infiltrate the deserter group and betray them to the authorities. After hearing Bat's story of Jerry's murder and seeing his exempt status identification, they invited him to their secluded camp on a small island on Leaf River. Here, Bat learned more of the atrocities on dissenters and deserters. They discussed the effect of the latest act of Congress on conscription laws. The men of the deserter group were not ruffians or renegades. They were of all classes: farmers, businessmen, professional men, students and some professional soldiers. The confederate armies were fighting and losing battles. The manpower and strength were dwindling. Enlistments were expiring and the government was offering fifty dollars to any man who would re-enlist. This had but little results. Congress had then written into law a conscription act inducting men between the ages of 18 to 35 for three years. The measure had drawn instant fire in the South. However, one positive result was to create a burst of volunteering by men who preferred to sign up for the local militia, hoping duty around home rather than marching off to war among strangers.

Bat remained with the deserter group for a number of days and was amazed at the growing numbers joining them every day. He listened to their complaints of the government, the Conscription Act, the inequitable "exemption" program and new stories of atrocities on deserters.

The corruption brought on by the unreasonable exemptions appeared to be a basic problem motivating desertions. The "hardscrabble" farmers in the group pointed out there was not a single exemption for the farmer, regardless of how many hungry mouths he left behind to go to war.

There, indeed, was a long list of exemptions by which draftees might avoid service. These measures favored the wealthy and influential. One section of the law permitted "substitutions"; a person not liable for duty may be relieved as a substitute for those who were. This allowed anyone with money to pay a man to serve for him. And fifty thousand draftees did so. The price ranged from sixteen hundred dollars plus a fine horse to as high as five thousand dollars. Some even offered large acreage of farmland. This opened opportunity for speculators to make thousands by helping "sell a man"; connive in his desertion, and sell him over and over again. One person told of a man who had sold himself, working on his own, twenty times.

There were a number of ways to dodge the draft if one had the right job or some influence. The long list of "legally employed" included mail carriers, telegraph operators, newspaper printers, apothecary, teacher of 20 or more pupils, ministers, railroad hands, munitions workers, tanners, blacksmiths, cotton mill workers and wheelwrights. If a man was not influential to get an "exemption" job he became food for powder. Thousands of men, however, simply ignored the summons. At the end of 1863, the roster for the entire confederate army numbered 464,000 men. In fact, only 278,000 men remained on duty, and 187,000 AWOL. There was, therefore, no doubt in the mind's of the deserters a "rich man's war and a poor man's fight."

There developed a severe unrest among the people of "hog and corn" economy, the "hardscrabble" farmers, and the troops on duty. To make matters worse, the Congress adopted perhaps the most controversial exemption measure of all: the so-called "Twenty-Negro Law." This law deferred from service any planter or overseer on plantations with more than twenty slaves. In effect, it exempted the slave's owners who brought the war on in the first place. The law aroused a spirit of rebellion throughout the South and especially in Mississippi. It also aroused the rich to ingenious evasions. Plantation owners divided their slaves into gangs of 20 or more, put them on separate tracks of land, and made their sons and other relative's overseers to protect them from conscription. The poor man became angrier and banded together to resist.

As the hide-away on Leaf River swelled with newcomers, discussions and more instances of scheming revealed, caused more bitterness among the group of deserters and dissenters. They swore they would be shot before they would fight for a country where the rich man's property is to be taking care of and those who have none are to go fight first. Any thought Bat may have had to eventually enlist and fight for the Confederacy had rapidly deteriorated. He decided to abandon the idea of running down Jerry's murderers, as this seemed insignificant in light of the multiple atrocities revealed by the newly arrived deserters. He was concerned, however, as to the direction of the ultimate disposition of this belligerent band of good people.

The group of deserters soon had a leader, a Newton Knight from Meridian county seat of Jones County, who was conscripted into the 7th Mississippi regiment. A unionist at heart, Knight refused to fight and was allowed to serve as a hospital orderly. He became discontented and abandoned his regiment for the woods and swamps along Leaf River, near Laurel. Their Jasper Collins, another deserter, who was outraged over the "20-negro exemption" provision of the conscription law, joined him. By mid 1862, the two had recruited about 100 unyielding dissentious deserters and made contact with the band Bat was hanging out with. Knight organized the dissenting groups into what he called the "Republic of Jones" with the purpose to form a home defense band for resistance to opposition by assassination, raiding, destruction and other means to save families from famine.

Led by Knight, the dissenters lived up to there charter. They quickly won popular sympathy by their concern for the poor. Food shortages were severe. Shortage of labor was a grave problem. Men from farms had joined the armed forces, as they had no exemptions. Acreage was cut, as farmlands became battlefields. Food production had transportation problems. Where it was abundant, it rotted in the fields for lack of transportation to the market. Even when limited transportation was available, farmers often refused to bring their produce to town for fear of "impressments" officers. There was hunger and near starvation in some parts of the Confederacy, especially in Mississippi. Areas near the battle lines were most often swept clean of all food. Foragers from both sides preyed upon the land. City dwellers were forced to do without the simplest of foods. Inhabitants resorted to eating refuse from garbage cans.

Conditions in some counties in Mississippi were appalling and unparalleled. There was barely enough food to sustain life and people were reduced to beggary. Meat shortage was most acute during the entire conflict. The scarcity of food, the absence of men butchers and pork curers, lack of salt, all combined to produce shortages. When the federals closed the Rio Grande in Texas it cut off the supply of Texas beef. One ounce of meat per person in a household, daily was considered ample for the times. Fish and fowl were substitutes. Sugar supply almost disappeared when the Federals took Louisiana.

As to clothes, when cows were killed for meat their hides were converted to shoes. Medicine, as well as physicians, were numbered among the acute shortages. Because of the call to duty the number of physicians and surgeons left at home was insufficient to meet demands. Often only one doctor was left to serve an entire county.

These were the conditions that sparked the "Republic of Jones" to "secede" from the State of Mississippi. This group, led by Newton Knight, made their headquarters in a cave they called "The Devil's Den," situated on an island on Leaf River. From this refuge they went forth to sink ferryboats, burn bridges and bushwhack Confederates along the roads. Tales of their undaunted exploits circulated until the gangs first entered legend as the "Free State of Jones," and free its soldiers remained, working their skill in deadly fashion. When Confederate detachments tried to catch Knight's men, the fugitives either ambushed the horsemen or melted into the swamps. Sometimes, small Confederate parties sent to capture the deserters often joined them.

Bat rode and fought with this band of men and became respectful of both Jasper Collins and Newton Knight, although never making any effort to cultivate their acquaintance or camaraderie. He felt he was very much a misplaced person, still in civilian clothes, carrying an "exempt" card, which would shield him from deserter atrocity were he to fall into the hands of the Confederates. He figured he could always declare impressments or victim of coercion, were he captured with the dissenters.

Nevertheless, Bat felt a strong loyalty to the group's cause and bitterness towards that of the Confederacy. He was motivated to go on raids and marauding exploits by the agony experienced in the outright murder of his friend, Jerry. Bat continued to ride with them, never feeling any wrong, but only sympathy for the plight of the people suffering a useless war.

As the war progressed, they raided in nearby counties. In Jasper County on one particular raid, they came into a group of six wagons and fifteen men with loads of corn. The men were enjoying themselves in a local bar. Only a few escaped into the woods. Newton threatened the bartender with death if he gave one drop of liquor to the deserters. He gave the corn to Irish families who were pro-union and starving. Such exploits earned Knight's men the reputation as "robin hoods" of Mississippi. Too, some deserters, as many as 40 or 50 men at a time, would go to farms and help on the farms. They would never prey on a farm. The Confederate atrocities against families of deserters sat up a favorable position or status for the deserters. In general, the deserters were feared and respected in Jones County. Cavalry patrols often fled on knowledge of their nearness.

Lt. General Polk decreed in 1862 all deserters who gave up would be given amnesty, but few responded. By 1864, it was clear that the deserters were out of hand. Shortly thereafter, Colonel Maury, with 200 sharp shooting troops and horse artillery invaded Ellisville, the county seat of Jones. There followed a series of engagements. During March and April 1864, these engagements took place at Rocky Creek, Big Creek Church, Hebron Lodge, Reddocks Ferry and Knights Mill. General Polk changed his amnesty proclamation and ordered punishment for all deserters, as they had inflicted heavy losses on Colonel Maury's sharpshooters during these engagements. One deserter caught was offered amnesty if he would return to his old outfit responded, "hell no—I'll shoot everyone. I'll shoot every chance I get as long as I live." He and his brothers were hanged.

The Confederates closed in on Jones County. Knight set up Ellisville as the capitol of the "Free State of Jones" and here, on one Sunday morning the Confederates surrounded a church and captured a number of Knight's men. Bat was among the group but was released when he showed his exemption card and advised he was on a cotton-buying trip for the Corinth mill. As he rode away, he turned to observe four young men being hanged in front of the town's people. They drove a wagon out from under them. Bat, secluded himself in a nearby thicket, and saw them proceed to hand over nine other men, all with whom Bat had rode on various raids. Later, in Demopolis, while riding alone, he witnessed the outright murder of an old man for desertion.

Bat made his way back to "headquarters" at the Devil's Den. A few weeks later the confederates sent 44 bloodhounds into the swamps seeking the whereabouts of the deserter band. Forty-two dogs were killed by poisoned meat and ground glass. But many deserters were found and a number of young men were captured and strung up. In one instance, a 12-year-old boy, refusing to tell of the deserter's whereabouts, was strung up three times, bullets shot by his head, before being released. Not far away from their hideout, another deserter visiting his wife and children was apprehended and shot in front of his wife. In Meridian, Ben Knight, Newton's cousin at home on furlough, was mistakenly taken for Newton and hanged in front of his family.

Unfortunately for Knight's band, a few loyal to the Confederacy infiltrated the deserter group. Newton's army, at a wedding at Cracker's Neck near Leaf River just after Christmas 1864, were surprised by a hundred man Confederate cavalry Patrol. Newton was wounded seriously, but most of the deserters, including Bat, were saved as they fled pell-mell into the swamps.

Time was running out on the army of the "Free State of Jones," their final skirmish took place January 10, 1865, at Salt's Battery, where the deserters had sworn their oath almost two years earlier.

Newton Knight led a charmed life. Dogs, horses, cavalry came close to ending his operations on several occasions, but he survived. Before the war ended, a few months after the Salt's Battery skirmish, most of the band returned to their homes in Jones County. Survivors, along with Newton, numbered about 20 men, including Bat. Newton was never tried or punished, nor was any of the surviving band. They had fought against policies that proved grossly inequitable and finally intolerable. Bat was not particularly proud of his role during the conflict and rarely spoke of it in later years. He had returned to Corinth after Salt's Battery, a bitter and disappointed man. He was battle weary and hardened to a way of life that left him in doubt and little confidence he could ever return to the normal human being he had considered himself before becoming involved with the "Jones County Deserters." The only cause he felt he fought for was a right to be different, and this by being a "Southern Yankee." He had never once worn a service uniform, nor had he during the two-year duration of his activity encountered a union soldier.

He found Corinth devastated, a victim of the disastrous stand of the Confederate Army. Approximately, 78,000 men from Mississippi had served on the Confederate forces. Thirty-six percent did not live to return. Twelve thousand fell in battle and 15,000 died of diseases. Whole units were slaughtered. For example, the 6th regiment went into the battle at Shiloh with 425 men. Three hundred became casualties. At Antietam, the 16th regiment lost sixty-three percent. The 29th regiment lost fifty-three percent at Chickamauga. The Vicksburg cadets marched off with one hundred twenty-three men, only six came back. The Vicksburg Sharpshooters left with one hundred twenty-four men and only one returned.

War-time destruction of physical facilities, buildings, railroads, towns and villages were capricious. Jackson was practically burned to the ground. Corinth looked like a ghost town. Bat was hesitant to even show himself. He was certain his reputation of being neither a serviceman nor a deserter, but a civilian renegade, had preceded him home, and it had. When he called upon the Tuckers with hope of seeing Etta alive and well, he was promptly ordered off the premises.

BUFFALO KILLING ON OPEN RANGE

Chapter Ten

BUFFALO HIDE HUNTERS

In the year 1864, a young hunter had been killing buffalo to supply the army with meat. He shipped the hides to New York City to see if they would sell. The tannery spotted them and paid 3.50 each and ordered 2000 more at the same price. The new tanning process made hides collected any time of the year useable.

The stampede for hide hunters was spawned. The staked plains, where buffalo were in great numbers became a hide hunter's paradise. Hide hunters organized. Christian Sharp, invented a heavy rifle calibrated to 1000 yards, which could drop a buffalo at 600 to 700 yards, and a good marksman could kill up to 250 animals a day.

Dodge City became the center of the trade. As loaded wagons converged on the new railroad, whorehouses put up signs "no buffalo hunters," they stink.

One evening while Bat and his comrades were holed up in their Leaf River camp, a person named Nixon related a buffalo story that changed Bat's career. Nixon told of an episode when he killed 120 buffalo in a single stand in forty minutes time, and in 38 days he killed 2173 animals for which he collected $3 per hide. Nixon insisted this was a true story. He further explained how the buffalo helped along its own slaughter, that although the sight of man frightened the animal, it was not frightened by the report of a gun. When a concealed hunter dropped one buffalo, others, smelling blood rushed around the fallen animal, and the entire drove could be wiped out. Furthermore, Nixon went on, one experienced hunter could skin up to 100 animals in a day, and the hides brought $3 each on the Dodge City Market. That's a lot of money, thought Bat.

Bat decided to outfit a crew, as well as himself, and go into the business. He slipped away from Corinth and made his way out of Mississippi into Texas. One month later he made known his presence at the Lobo's Den in Lobo, Texas.

Bat was a handsome young man of 20, stalwart, with an hourglass figure. He was of somber countenance, and the appearance of a perpetual pout. Utoka Jett took a liking to Bat on first sight. They spent many evenings together. He discussed his ambitions to be a buffalo hunter, and she threatened him to never appear in her establishment, if he took up the trade. This did not set well with Bat. He disappeared from the Lobo's Den and was not heard from for several months. Utoka missed him dearly, as she had become quite fond of his presence.

Bat outfitted himself, and in a three-month period gained considerable funds from his trade. He was determined to return to Lobo and go into competition with Utoka. He arranged for lumber and supplies to be shipped up from Big Springs, and with Mexican labor he constructed a gambling hall and saloon next door to the Lobo's Den. Utoka was furious. For the grand opening, Bat imported dance hall girls, gamblers, and entertainers. He siphoned off the trade and customers of the den in quick order. Though buffalo hunters were held in low esteem, Bat welcomed them to his brothel. To gain favor with the ladies of the night, Bat fashioned a "vat", complete with running water, in which the hunters would submerge themselves in creosote, killing all odor, and meeting the ladies squeaky clean. Bat's "vat" became famous.

He expanded his hide trade. The nearest rail siding had been Dodge City. Now, the Texas-Pacific had inched its way into Fort Worth, only 200 miles away. There was a suitable wagon road over which heavy loads of hides could be hauled from Lobo to Ft. Worth. Bat outfitted two parties of hunters with wagons, horses, oxen, guns and ammunition and supplies. He agreed to pay Dodge City prices in cash for hides brought in. The venture was successful. Bat became rich, and bought out the struggling Lobo's Den. Utoka was broke, and connected firmly in the "madam" business with Bat.

The great slaughter of the buffalo was now going full blast, Dodge City was booming with the trade. Some hunters were working as far down the Panhandle as Red River, to be in a position to intercept the great southern herds. To combat northern competition, and to get his share of the northern migration, Bat went to Adobe Walls, Texas on the Canadian River to recruit hide hunters for his venture. He outfitted the crew with the new and improved heavy caliber rifles, which would help along the buffalo destruction. In view of the improved guns, and the railroads supplying ready transportation, grisly commercial hunters were flocking to the plains to earn wages gathering hides, meat, bones, and tallow. This activity, obviously, would continue until the last of the herds were gone.

ASIDE:

At the beginning of the 19th century it was estimated there were six million buffalo on the great plains of America. At the beginning of the 2oth century there were 300.

In the meantime, the Indians were outraged at the slaughter. Under the leadership of Chief Quanah Parker, the chiefs put together a war party of 8000 Macaws, Apaches, and

Comanche warriors. They gathered at Adobe Walls, where Bat and twenty-eight hunters had forted up with their .50 cal. long barrel buffalo rifles. They had a distinct advantage on the Indians; however 28 men against 8000 narrowed the odds for survival. The hunters repelled attack after attack, killing 180 warriors and over 200 wounded. As the tribe leaders sat their mounts on a cliff overlooking the forted hunters, a young chief on a fidgety paint kept prancing about waving a feathered spear. Bat remarked; "is there anyone in here who can pick off that smartaleck? If we could do that at this distance they would leave," Bat said. The distance was about 600 yards. One man stepped forward. "I can do it, and I will take bets on it," he said loudly. With all bets in he awaited the smartaleck Chief to stand still. Then he let off a booming shot and the Indian hit the ground. The other chiefs immediately withdrew their forces and moved away. Bat approached the rifleman, "I'd like to know your name, that shot was amazing." "Name's Bat Masterson, Sir."

Bat returned to Lobo and expanded his group of hunters. The venture was so successful that Lobo was labeled the hide hunters capital. 8 and 10 yoke of oxen pulled four and six hitches of wagons over the road to Fort Worth, grinding soil in the deep ruts to powder. During this period a lieutenant Bullis, with a company of federal cavalrymen, soundly defeated Quanah Parker at Cedar Lake, driving the tribe to take refuge in the Palo Duro Canyon, near Amarillo.

The population of Lobo tripled. The Lobo's Den was violent and lawless and lewd. Of the 100 women there, less than half dozen could lay claim to decency. Bat was growing richer by the day. At one time he had 20,000 flint-cured hides spread out on 3 acres of ground. It took all winter to transport them to Fort Worth. Between 1866 and 1882 the buffalo was virtually destroyed. There was never known to be a more shameless butchery of animal life. Without protective cover, the plains animals were defenseless. Trails and grassland above the great salt licks, east of the Red River bear testimony of the migration of these heavy plodding beasts. At the beginning of the 19th century there were possibly 6 million buffalo grazing back and forth in the grassland of the west. They grazed in separate herds, the bulls together, and the cows and calves going their separate ways, except during breading season. Where the buffalo were found there was always water and grass. Adobe Walls, on the south fork of the Canadian River, signifies in history the beginning of the demise of the Comanche and the end of the buffalo. In 1871, Quanah Parker and a party of young men rode south from the Canadian river to Blanco Canyon and discovered the buffalo slaughter. They were outraged and proceeded to raid Col. McKenzie's camp in protest. McKenzie retaliated. Quanah and his band of 400 men, women, and children were trapped in the Palo Duro Canyon, where they surrendered, and walked to the reservation at Fort Sill, Oklahoma.

CATTLE BARON
HORSEMAN—ARISTROCRAT

Chapter Eleven

CATTLE BARON

AND

THE PASSING OF AN ERA

When Will Purdy was mustered out of service; it had been four years since he last saw Utoka Jett. He left her standing on the wind swept porch of Lobo's Den, where she was engaged as a "madam". It was that same porch where four years ago he dropped his saddle and gear after an exhausting trek thru the night, around Cedar Lake, to avoid the Comanches. She was a vision of loveliness, the memory of which sustained him to a great extent as he endured two years of imprisonment in an open stockade near Santa Fe. Now he was back, as he promised. His previous stay in Lobo was short, only a matter of a few days, during which time he was forced to gun down a couple of hired guns who reported to a lavish beauty named Vashti. It seems Vashti ran her own empire of cattle rustlers, hiding behind and posing as the wife of a Texas cattle baron, Josh Epps. Will had no opportunity to meet her husband, Josh, whom he had heard much about. A mountain man, trapper, turned wagon train guide, then cattle drover, and from this profession he had amassed large herds of his own, and had leased thousands of acres of lush grassland from the State of Texas. Josh was a powerhouse in the West, and a most respected Cattle Baron. As to his wife, Vashti, that was another story. Josh Epps, now was a cattle baron with the largest spread on the Texas western frontier. All of this was accomplished midst an epidemic of cattle rustling, marauding, renegade Comanches, and lawlessness of every description. Before Will could meet this legendary character, the war came along and snatched him away. He thought much on this situation, Josh, Vashti, Utoka during the two years held in an outdoor stockade prison, suffering thru two severe winters, watching others die. Then to top this disastrous period in his life, the disgraceful defeat of Sibley's entire 4th regiment, including his own company of rangers. What next in my young life, mused Will. I'm only 36 and already lived two lifetimes. Now, out of service, and back in the saddle, life is wonderful, just being alive!

Will had no desire to return to the ranger organization. It would not be like before. His loss of friend, Rip Ford, wore heavily on his mind. He went to the corral, selected a horse as he was privileged to do, saddled up, and rode west.

Will could not deny the urge to return to the Lobo's Den and, hopefully, Utoka Jett. It had been four years since he left her there on the porch, a look of apprehension on her countenance, the pools of blue slightly cloudy. That vision sustained him while near death as a P.O.W. It's worth returning to. He sensed a slight palpitation of the heart. Then there's Vashti, the glamorous vixen of the saddle. He couldn't envision her being anything else than a hard driving baroness with an ulterior motive. She's dangerous, he thought. Nevertheless, she hired me, thinking I was a fast-gun on the lose. Wonder what she had in mind. Well, let's find out. I'll just ride up and say "ah'm back, ready to go to work, where do I start?"

He spurred his horse forward to a brisk lope. Got a good week's ride, he smiled. A new life, embellished with a tinge of the old, beckoned him.

In less than a week, Will tossed the rains over the hitching rack at the Lobo: I'm Back!

RETURN TO THE LOBO'S DEN

Nothing about the Lobo's Den appeared familiar, even the front had changed. New sign depicted a Lobo Wolf, tongue hanging out, rolling his eyes at scantily dressed dancing girls. At one end was a large sketch of a black-headed madam, Utoka. Will sat for a long moment and stared at the colorful front. He felt a strange sensation sweeping over him. That there was more to that sign than met his eye. The "den" appeared twice the size. When he first met Utoka on the porch, four or five years ago, she did not appear to be the "madam" now depicted by the sign. The decorative billboard was conveying something to him he had rather not attempt to interpret.

Will dismounted and ambled through the swinging doors, and experienced a slight flutter of the heart. It was the time of the afternoon when activity began reving up for the evening. There were now two bartenders in the den, both busily polishing glassware, mirrors, and the mahogany bar. One glanced casually at Will, eyeing him as another drifter dropping in for a drink and satisfy his curiosity, obviously sparked by the inviting saloon sign. A pall of smoke lingered over a table occupied by four men with cards; three men stood nearby, drinks in their hands, pistols slung low on the thigh, tied down, an indication this was not just a hangout for the average cow poke. He stealthily sideled up to the bar, planting a booted foot on the brass rail, and before he could order a drink, she burst thru an ornamented door, mouth open as if to address the bartenders, but instead of orders, she uttered a gasp, "Will", she blurted. "Utoka", he responded. They embraced. Her slightly perfumed body sent him reeling. What a sensation, just to encircle his arms around her sensuous body. Softest thing he had ever held, though only for a brief moment. Following, suddenly behind Utoka came a handsome young man in his mid twenty's. "Oh, Will, I want you to meet my partner, Bat." Howdys were cordially exchanged, and Will motioned for a drink. Utoka, ignoring the brush off, touched his arm gently, and said, "please join me for a drink, I have lots to tell you." "I bet," said Will coolly.

Utoka related events that had occurred over the past four years in the Cedar Lake territory, including Josh and Vashti's relations at his growing ranch holdings; the Lobo's Den and it's merger with Bat the buffalo hide hunter, and of the shocking demise of Pelham Ware, so called vagabond guitar player. It seems Ware turned out to be an under-cover agent for the Cattleman's Association, a fast gun planted at the den to get a line on the cattle rustlers that continued to plague and outrage the ranchers. Seems his findings involved Vashti. When confronted by Ware, Josh shot him and rescued Vashti from the law. Josh has repeatedly denied her involvement, and to this day she is an obvious control of the lawless element raiding the ranges. Josh's herd's continued to grow, others diminished. "That should tell you something," Will said.

"Bat showed up here before the war ended. I figured he was a deserter from the Confederacy, but no one cared about that. He went heavily into the hide business and did quite well; built a saloon next to mine, and we merged our businesses. It had boomed. Bat is quite a "go-getter". Must be, thought Will, wonder what he's up to with Utoka. He was afraid to ask.

Then to Will's utter surprise she looked him straight into his one exposed eye, and said: "Will, I am not a madam, as such. I am a plant. Been with Pinkerton, since the day you and I met. The Cattlemen engaged the agency to break up the cattle rustling. I was told the Governor would give me some assistance by sending a Texas Ranger. He never showed, then the war, and that was that."

Will gulped, "think that will come about?" he asked. "No, and I resigned from Pinkerton and joined Bat in his enterprises. We get along, and I got tired of being pawed over by trashy gunmen who were hanging out with Vashti, at old man Epps spread. Did you know he was almost killed and is paralyzed from waist down?" "The wedding they planned never took place. Vashti is completely in charge," retorted Utoka disgustedly. "Somebody's got to nail her," she stated flatly.

Will hung around for several days, attempting to avoid as many people as possible. He was easily recognizable, by the patch over his eye. The death of Pelham Ware bothered him. Something doesn't smell right.

Will was becoming more disenchanted with himself, daily. Here he was, without a job, hanging around the Lobo's Den, moon-eyed over Utoka, who was, ostensibly, more than just a partner with Bat, and disturbed over news of Vashti. After all, Vashti hired him the day before he took off for the ill-fated western expedition. Maybe I should go back and check out this Lazy "V" situation. But, I'm not a Ranger anymore. If I go to work for Vashti, I've got to join'em. He sat down with both Utoka and Bat, they had dinner, and talked long into the evening. Something about Will I like, thought Bat.

Don't know why, but I have a strange feeling Bat and I have something in common, Will thought to himself. Wish he wasn't so thick with Utoka, and vice versa.

It was late in the day when Will took off on the 20 plus miles to the Lazy "V". He had to have the right responsive urge to make the trip. A foreboding sensation engulfed him when he saddled up and hit the trail. To meet Vashti after four years would be an experience; also, the unknown status of Josh intrigued him. Was he incapacitated? Senile? Mean and belligerent? He had never met the legend and was not all that anxious to do so. The very thought of the meeting left Will with a feeling he did not comprehend.

Dusk was approaching by the time Will came within a mile of the ranch house. He paused at a roadside feed barn, a part of the Lazy "V"; it would not be to his most favorable liking to show up at dark; would not afford him the best of appearance. He turned to the barn and rode thru the partially opened door. Inside were ample bales of hay for the horse's food and a place to bed down. He unsaddled and prepared to spend the night. Hope Vashti doesn't find out about this.

At break of dawn, the horse was up and pawing the hay covered floor, obviously, looking for water. There was none available. Will stretched and looked out the door towards the house. He was startled to see a rider approaching in a leisurely gallop. To his surprise, it was a woman, Vashti. He quickly saddled, mounted, and moved back concealed by the door. Vashti approached, at the proper moment he spurred his horse into her path, grabbing it by the bits. The startled horse writhed and twisted, Vashti grabbed frantically for leather. She screamed, "you bastard, that's a good way to get killed, if I hadn't been grabbing for the horn it would have been for my gun and you would be dead!" she gasped. "Will Purdy." He smiled calmly and said, "hi, kid, I'm back to take up that job." They both quickly dismounted and went inside the barn.

What a beauty! He felt his groin on fire. He spontaneously clutched her with a bear hug and planted his mouth squarely on hers. She did not resist, but melted in his arms. They sank to the soft hay. Sometime later they rolled over and came up for air. "Now, let's talk", said Will. "Why?" and she pulled him down to the hay bed.

On the ride to the ranch house Will asked, "how much of this goes with my job?" "As much as you can take, big boy," she retorted. Things are looking up, just waiting for the other boot to fall. It's too good to be true.

Josh had already gone on his early morning ride in the under-slung buckboard, his own invention, enabling him to get in and out of the conveyance without assistance. It was noon when he returned. Will was awaiting him at the ranch house gate.

"Name's Will Purdy, missed you first time I came out here four years ago." "Yah, I know about you, my kind of man. What happened to your eye?" "A birthmark from childhood," said Will. Josh gasped. He was so startled, Will asked if he was alright. "I'm ok; if you'd seen me 4 years ago you would have seen a complete man. Now I'm not even half a man. Not much good to anybody but myself, I reckon." "You've seen Vashti?" "Yep, this morning." "She'd been my wife," . . . he shook his head sadly. Will felt a slow burn, which he hoped wasn't obvious, "The barn!" thank heaven she was not his wife.

"Come in and let's sit a spell. Tell me about yourself," said Josh. "I mean let's go way back, back to the birthmark." Will grinned. Josh stared at the ground. This bothered Will, he's acting kinda strange. Slipping into his wheel chair, Will took the handles and pushed him up the ramp to the porch. Josh put a hand on Will's with a slight pat. A teardrop fell, but Will did not see it. He only noticed some rapid blinking of the ole man's eyes.

They talked late into the day. Will now had a pretty good handle on the ranch activity and the scope of his empire. He thought Josh went overboard and told him a lot more than was necessary. When they parted Will went to the bunkhouse for dinner and the shaken old cattle baron slipped thru a swinging door to his supper. Vashti thought he was unusually quiet. She avoided conversation still sensualizing over the morning event.

Josh, accompanied by Vashti, proceeded to complete his ranch house mansion at Cedar Lake. He had spent years stock-piling lumber freighted in from Big Springs, to prepare for the constructing and it required two years to build out. The house was nearing completion, and she and Josh and Will made a visit.

"One of these days we will get moved and have one heck-uva housewarming" exulted Vashti. That day appears months away, thought Will. It would fall his lot to relocate the bunkhouses, outbuildings, feedlots, corrals, and support facilities. He looked forward to the job. He sensed this opportunity to remain aloof from the unsavory crew of cowmen on Vashti's payroll, without being too obvious. Too, it was closer in to the town of Lobo where he could chance a visit with Utoka. The thought of the handsome Bat ever present disturbed him.

Several months passed with Will remaining fairly aloof from the other hands. They figured something weird about this one-eyed gunman, and they kept their distance. Too, it was obvious that he had an inside track with the big house. He was observed going on long rides with Josh, jogging along side the under-sling buckboard. Also, the wayside barn about a mile up the road seemed to be off limits to everyone but Vashti and Will. They insisted on putting out the feed for the special breed of heifers penned there.

Lawlessness continued to prevail on the open range, and ranchers continued to be outraged at nothing being done about it. Strange that no robberies, thefts, or violations seem to ever occur on the Lazy "V". Cattlemen cast a wary eye in that direction, but careful to make no accusations. However, on a special occasion Will and Vashti rode into Lobo. They stopped at the Den for a drink. Bat and Utoka were nowhere around, and whereabouts unknown. Bat was known to disappear for days at a time being the businessman he was. But unusual was Utoka's absence. Will viewed this with mixed emotions as he had become quite fond of Vashti and likewise. Endearing thoughts of Utoka had practically vanished from Will's thoughts. He was kind of glad they were away.

Joe Thorpe, the well-known cattle drover, thundered into the Lobo's Den. The big man was outraged. He had brought a herd of 3000 through Lobo two days ago and had incurred a loss of 500 head. An Indian raid had stampeded his herd, and he and his men were still rounding up the scattered herd. He could account for at least 500 missing. Joe bellied up to the bar with Will and in conversation, he learned of his and Josh's past relations. He told Will that in all due respect for Josh, he had advised his men to stay clear of the Lazy "V" which laid several miles to the east of the drovers trail. Not likely 500 cattle would stray that faraway and all in one direction. Will took it upon himself to invite Joe to visit the area for a look-see, but when he advised Vashti of the invitation, she bristled. Joe bowed out and left the den.

On the return to ranch headquarters, Vashti was strangely silent. Will wondered about the disappearance of the 500. Joe said "Indians" had made a raid and that would surely rule out the Lazy "V". But would it? Indians? What would they do with a herd of 500? They don't operate that way. He pondered the situation, and upon return to the bunkhouse, he launched a search for Indian costumes and found the cache in the loft. It was possible his own men, disguised as Indians had pulled the raid, stampeding the herd and cutting out the 500. Where are the cattle?

Will put 14 hours in the saddle before overhauling Joe Thorpe and his men, pushing the 2500 remaining herd north to Dodge City. Joe selected three riders to accompany him and Will for a search out on the Lazy "V". Two days later they found the 500, intact grazing in an isolated section of the Lazy "V" just below the rim of the Cap Rock. They surprised three gunmen, rustlers, and took them to a nearby tree to mete out range justice. The type known to every cattle thief; hanging by the neck until dead. Will recognized two of the men as Vashti's hired hands, the other a stranger. Both men winked at Will with a knowing glance. This infuriated Will, but he showed no emotions, made no comment, or gave Joe any indication he knew the men. They surmised these were professional rustlers and had this secluded pasture staked out for laundering stolen herds.

Will had a terrible choice to make. Proceed to hang the men, Joe take his cattle, and Will go home and keep his mouth shut, protecting the woman he loved from disgrace and prison; or, take the men captive, confront Josh and Vashti and turn them into the cattlemen's association for prosecution. It was too much for Will to handle. He conferred with Joe.

Big-hearted Joe took compassion upon Will. He also expressed remorse over Josh's plight, his health, in his immobility, and inability to stay abreast of his fast-moving "care-giver". Joe had never met Vashti, but commiserated with Will's feelings for her. Then imparting his great wisdom, gained from the rigors of his outdoor life, good ole Joe proposed a workable plan. They would extract a confession from the three rustlers in exchange for their lives, and get the unadulterated goods on Vashti, and her men. Call a countywide meeting of neighboring ranchers, rendezvous at Josh's home, and hold a confab. Let the ranchers decide the fate of the lazy "V", obviously stocked by thousands of contraband cattle taken from other ranchers. As to the hired gun hands, turn them over to the law for appropriate prosecution. As to the fate of Vashti and that of she and Will's future, just have faith, justice will be done, and steel yourself to accept the consequences.

During the confessing they learned that Vashti had picked this very spot to process her stolen cattle; that she, at one time, was followed to the place by a guy on a horse carrying a guitar. A peculiar looking guy; could never figure him out. He took special care not to be seen by Vashti. That figures, thought Will. The beginning of the end for Pelham Ware, cattleman's detective.

Will took the three rustlers to Fort Loop and had them jailed for safekeeping. Lt. McKenzie was infuriated at the white men disguising themselves, and perpetrating atrocities as Indians. It was tough enough trying to keep the settlers from waging war on the Comanches. To punish them for their normal marauding episodes, but to frame them for lawlessness of the white man was unacceptable. McKenzie promised cooperation, and offered to be present at the rendezvous if Will requested.

Will, now a full-fledged foreman of the Lazy "V", worked outside of Vashti's knowledge in setting up the rendezvous. He dispatched his riders in all directions carrying the invitation to "open house" celebration of Josh's newly completed ranch headquarters at Cedar Lake. Vashti was ecstatic over the "open house" date now finalized. If only she knew!

The open house rendezvous, planned by Joe and Will, fell in place. All went well with the festivities, food, drink, and music. Joe had made it back from Dodge City to conduct the planned "hearing" and expose the purpose of the gathering. He suggested the merriment be cut short of inebriation, and get on with the gruesome task.

His voice boomed for attention. Everyone had gathered in the spacious courtyard, and of a special note, Lt. McKenzie's armed soldiers surrounded it. They seemed to have appeared out of nowhere. McKenzie himself had been a special guest mingling with the others, unnoticed. From the edge of darkness Bat and Utoka Jett appeared carrying a box, which they deposited at Joe's feet. They joined Will at the side of the garden. Vashti wheeled Josh to front and center, a quizzical expression emanating from her pretty face. She was not aware of any planned program and was puzzled at Joe's commanding appearance as suddenly being in charge. She glanced at Will, he avoided her gaze, and turned to Bat. They exchanged looks of anxiety. Utoka stood stiff and silently, a stern look from narrowed pools of blue.

Joe spoke, "I lost 500 head from my herd a few months ago passing thru these parts, marauding Indians. So happens I've come onto their garb and paraphernalia." He dumped the garments and headdress items from the box. So happens, men employed on the Lazy "V" wore these, and their boss is Vashti, our lovely hostess." A gasp went up from the audience. The men of the Lazy "V" shifted uneasily as if to make a break. "There's nowhere to go boys. We've seen to that," motioning to the armed guard. "Bring'em out soldiers," Joe shouted. Two armed soldiers brought before the people the three rustlers who openly confessed to the audience.

Will had no comprehension of the reaction of Vashti and Josh. He had agonized for days. Now it's happened and he reluctantly looked their way. Utoka clutched his hand. Bat placed his big hand in comfort on Will's shoulder. It was a sad sight, deathly silence. Joe just stood there letting the scene have its impact on the guest, mostly neighboring ranchers, and losers over the years. Josh broke the silence.

"Every rancher in this county who has been a victim of our malfeasance and lawlessness will be repaid two fold for every cow lost. If I have to break up the Lazy "V" and sell it off cow-by-cow, by heavens you are going to be repaid." Then he turned to Vashti who stood petrified, immovable, unemotional, frozen countenance. How could she just stand there like an inanimate object? Doesn't she have a conscious? Will was extremely perplexed, Utoka moved and turned away in disgust. "Look at that hard-hearted vixen," she retorted.

Vashti shocked the audience, by moving slowly from behind the wheel chair and bending serenely over Josh. She lifted his face to hers and gently caressed his quivering lips. "It will be alright darling," she whispered. She turned to face the guests, drew herself upright and like an animated statue stepped forward. She spoke, "let it be known here and now, I have managed the Lazy "V" for over four years on behalf of the finest gentleman one could know; I was greedy. I took your cattle every opportunity I had, and replaced our cattle that went to the market. I have made Josh wealthy at your expense. I've associated with scum so long I just plane feel dirty," she looked with disdain upon the array of hired guns standing before her, under guard. "I hope I never see the likes of you again, and I'm sure I won't". "The money I have taken from you is in the bank. Josh won't have to give up this place to pay you, and I have kept a record of who I stole from and how much. Josh will double the amount and return it to you." Then of all things, she raised both arms in open invitation and with a radiant smile said, "if nobody is going to arrest me, please join me in a drink. . . I want to especially toast Mr. Joe, here, and my good friend, Will Purdy." No one could believe what they were hearing. A brazen heartless character, or one of the most brilliant performances ever to inhabit the vast Texas frontier. What a lady!! What a legend!

Conclusion

Vashti's records were well maintained and documented, as she had promised. Not a single rancher questioned the settlement proffered by Josh and Vashti. Within the year all accounts of the illicit transactions had been settled. Josh celebrated by going into the little county seat town of Lamesa and consulting with a long-time lawyer friend, and state representative. Joe Merritt drew up a strange agreement covering Josh's material and tangible holdings. To Will and Bat the assets were equally divided. To Vashti went no assets. He told Joe their marriage had never been consummated and matrimony would play no part in his bequeath of assets. He admitted emphatically that he was aware of and had ample knowledge that both Will and Bat were his begotten sons. As to Josh he made one single request, and had Judge Joe Merritt promise on a bible that he would execute the special provision in the will: to wit: that upon Josh's demise his body would be interred at the fork of the Drovers trail, just south of Cedar Lake, in Gaines County. Here at the fork Josh on his first major drive by way of Lobo, made the decision to take the trail north and east of Cedar Lake rather than continue north to Dodge City. The decision was a turning point in Josh's, the legend's, life. At this juncture he built his cattle empire and grew in stature to be known in history as one of the giant cattle barons of the west.

As the buffalo killing declined, the little cow town of Lobo declined. The railheads cris-crossed Texas and the trail driving became unnecessary. In the past decade the cattle trailed through the Lobo to Dodge City area became the second most traveled cattle trail in the U.S.; and estimate of over one million longhorns and 100,000 mustangs were brought through, transforming Dodge City from the buffalo capitol to the cowboy capital of the west. The Chisholm Trail was forgotten, and Fort Lobo became the important trail town. Now the railroads were leaving all this behind. Trailing cattle was no more. The government abandoned Fort Lobo, and with the cowboys, buffalo hunters, and free spending soldiers gone, the Lobo's Den had no reason to exist. The town was abandoned, and the building, erected by Bat Morgan left behind and torn down. The Lobo area was soon to become the center of one of the foremost beef producing districts in Texas. Its economy was solidly linked to the ups and downs of the cattle business, the only major industry in that part of Texas. Bat and Utoka united in marriage, and moved to Dawson County where they filed for homestead, and started life all over. Little did they know their acres were sitting on oil. In the late 20th century, the Welch Oil fields at Cedar Lake became a lucrative venture. The homestead was in the very center of the field. The luck of Bat and Utoka continued to prevail. In 1953, the State Legislature authorized the erection of a monument to Quanah Parker, Comanche Chief, at Cedar Lake near the site of Josh Epps' Lazy "V" spread.

The Indians were subdued and defeated at Palo Duro Canyon, and returned to reservation at Fort Sill, Oklahoma. The Texas panhandle became a vast unknown and empty land of interminable distance, stretching away to the horizon in every direction, the silence broken only by the wind moaning over the prairies, and the barking of the coyotes and wolves.

But not for long, in little more than a decade the Texas panhandle was cut-up, seized, fought over and parceled out to the strong. In the late 1800's people filed for one to four sections of land for homes. They came in wagons and built half-dugouts, shacks, or small houses for families. They plowed the land with one row plows, and planted maize, corn and peas. Some cotton, but lack of proximity to a gin discouraged cotton planting.

The land department of the state of Texas rescinded 60,000 acres of grassland that composed the Lazy "V". It became a part of the giant XIT ranch granted to a British syndicate in exchange for building the state capitol at Austin out of red granite. The huge XIT ranch sprawled across three million acres in 10 counties of the panhandle. It later became the Yellow Sod Company, parceled out and sold to the growing population of the south plains.

ASIDE:

Long on cattle but short on cash, like most ranchers, Charles Goodnight, famous drover, and cattleman went into partnership with John Adain, Englishmen and eventually 100,000 head of cattle ranged over a million acres. The ranch life was of frontier existence, and the era of the great ranches on the open range blazed briefly, little more than 20 years; but colored forever the popular image of west Texas. From the beginning, the open range was doomed by the industrial nation & desire for beef more palatable than that of the ranging longhorn. This called for better breading and the fencing of pastures. The XIT, and other large ranches, such as the Frying Pan, took the lead in stringing barbed wire across the panhandle. The wild free way of life in which cattle were simply turned loose to survive was transformed into a business in which cattle was tended.

Railroads provided the way to market. As cattle were fenced in, so were trails to market. Railroads brought settlers, wire, windmills and common truck for everyday commerce. The perceived value to society of the railroads shone through in the deal the state made with the Texas and Pacific Railway: The line received 20 sections—12,800 acres of public land, for each mile of track laid across the state.

With the demise or break-up of the Lazy "V" Josh appeared to give up. His health declined noticeably as ranchers came and went over the next year or so to settle their "alleged" losses. Vashti continued to give undivided attention and with docile attitude liquidated their obligations. Josh was buried at the fork in the trail as requested in his will, secluded in the high chaparral.

Vashti and Will married soon after the passing of Josh. They gave up their interest to the Lazy "V" by sale and moved to Lockhart, Texas. There Will established the overland freight line known as the Caddo Express. It ran in several directions, out of San Antonio and Lockhart. Vashti died of heart failure, unexpectedly, in 1899, and was buried at Big Foot, a nearby small town. She was 64 years old. On March 25, 1922 Will Purdy was walking to work and a car struck and killed him. He was 89 years old.

It was a passing of an era that reached back into the beginning of the "Lone Star State," retracing the steps of the Conquistadors, Indians, Cowboys, Rangers and other pioneering heroes and herdsmen. A state with one of the richest and most colorful past of any state. The past and the present surely exist side by side today.

The story of Josh, Will, Bat, Vashti, and Utoka combine to depict the bravery and the guts to form legendary significance for a coveted place on the memory shelves of history. They were truly Undaunted Adventurers.

Epilogue

This book, "Tales of the Undaunted", picks up segments of the formative years in American history. The stories related herein depicted akind of frontier adventure. Notwithstanding the fact that the whole history of America, in many respects, was a frontier adventure. Although the colorful characters comprising the genre of the "Tall Tales" is distinctly, for the most part, masculine, but the hardships of planting a new civilization was a family affair. This truly conveyed in the episode of the wagon trains, the taming of the Texas frontier; life in Cedar Lake under the constant peril and threat of marauding Comanches.

The Tall Tales selected for this book, embellishing the episodic careers of the "undaunted," were chosen for their historical significance. A factor that gives them legendary status. Stories relating to the early Americans who came to North America to carve out a life, most of whom were born in poverty; they came to escape poverty, only to find themselves enduring an isolated existence. They were of different nationalities, from a diverse society, unable to communicate except by signs and grunts and meaningful words spoken in numerous dialects. Common knowledge between the pioneers and the Native

Americans was impaired because there was but little to share. Decades passed and the courageous adventurous pioneers burrowed still deeper in the wilderness. During this period of natural isolation there surfaced a unique talented legendary teller of tall tales. This was the earliest form of education. They were celebrants. They attained legendary status by their own abilities to embellish a story and exaggerate. People for miles around came to hear them. They brought their children knowing that typically a good storyteller wrapped their tales in meaningful lessons of the times. Gatherings formed the basis of social, cultural and religious events and bonded families whom heretofore were strangers. These events generated understanding of matters that eventually became common knowledge far and wide. Throughout the vast American frontier, a sort of cultural literacy emerged that made a formidable force.

Years later a lone rider, wearing a dark patch over one eye was observed emerging from the High Chaparral, site of Josh's grave. He left a weather-beaten plank into which had been burned these words: YOUR HORSES WILL GALLUP PROUDLY IN HONOR OF YOUR BRAVE LIFE OF PERIL. "A fitting epitaph to the "Undaunted."

THE BLURB

Perhaps no legendary character stimulated the imagination of the settlement of the country than did the episodic career of Josh Epps. An illiterate mountain man turned wagon train guide, cattle drover, and baron of the vast plains of the Texas ranchlands. He gained legendary status due to the historical significance of his undaunted exploits and valor on the battlefield of the American wilderness. Josh's personality and ability to reel off an inexhaustible string of Tall Tales exaggerating his own episodes gave him legendary status; he was a celebrant among the itinerate teller of tall tales who brought cultural literacy to the settlers, burrowed deep in the wilderness. The tales of the undaunted characters associated with Josh Epps earned a permanent place on the shelves of the collective memory of the early pioneers. It is what made America, American. The undaunted frontiersman of Josh's day, ruled out fear, and survived at a time in history when staying alive was an achievement, and gaining success, a miracle.

THE BIO

Curtis Meeks was born into poverty, son of a sharecropper, in the year 1913. His father, former cavalryman was drafted into World War I leaving a wife and four siblings to struggle for a livelihood. The family drifted from farm to farm throughout his adolescent years; he attended several different one and two teacher schools. They survived the dust bowl of western Texas, and the Depression of the early 30's. He pursued a college education by living off campus in an abandoned chicken house until graduation. He was educated in finance at Tarleton State University, and in law at the University of Texas. He served in World War II as a gunnery officer in the Navy Air Corp, and went on to become a valued executive in Sears, Roebuck & Co. Upon retirement he was appointed chief financial officer of a major financial corporation, and later founded his own real estate holding company serving as chief executive officer. He lives in a retirement center in Orlando, widowed after 63 years of marriage to Janie Shirey, of Oklahoma City. In 1993 he was honored by his alma mater with the distinguished service award. He is a published author, the first book "Upward Bound" was released by Vantage Press in 1998.

Acknowledgements

Academic American Encyclopedia (Connecticut: Grolier)

Donald Worster, Dust Bowl—The Southern Plains in 1930's
(New York, Oxford press)

Frank Lawrence Owsley: King Cotton Diplomacy (Illinois
University of Chicago press)

John Ray Skatus, Mississippi . . . A bicentennial history
(New York, W. W. Norton & company)

John Foster. Southern Frontiersman. A story of Sam Dale
(New York: William morrow and Company)

Robert E. Corlew. Tennessee. A short History.
(Tennessee university press)

Paul M Anglo: The American Reader

E. P. Hirsch, Jr., Joseph E. Kett, James Trefal's
Dictionary Cultural Literacy

James M. McPherson; Alan Brinkley: Days of Destiny,
Crossroads in American History.

Photo of Joe Meek: Mrs. Frances A. Fuller, The River of the
West, R.W. Bliss and Co., 1870.

Illustrations: Jennifer T. Roper.

Photo of Texas Ranger: Walter Tucker Meeks.

BVG